Daniel Way (signature)

NEVER A DULL MOMENT

A Tapestry of Scenes & Stories from an Adirondack Medical Practice

TEXT AND PHOTOGRAPHS BY

DANIEL WAY, M.D.

EDITED BY

HARRIET BUSCH, M.D.

NEVER A DULL MOMENT

A Tapestry of Scenes & Stories from an Adirondack Medical Practice

Published by:
Indian Lake Press
PO Box 719, Indian Lake, NY 12842
www.danielway.com

ISBN 978-0-9899437-0-3 (soft)
ISBN 978-0-9899437-1-0 (hard)

Manufactured in the United States of America

DANIEL WAY, M.D., a native of Glens Falls, began taking pictures at the age of eleven and had already developed a passion for the art of photography long before beginning his career in family medicine for the Hudson Headwaters Health Network, which serves the entire southeastern Adirondacks. His first book is *All In A Day's Work, Scenes and Stories from an Adirondack Medical Practice.* His website is www.danielway.com

TABLE OF CONTENTS

FOREWORD

Lawrence Bauer, Chief Executive Officer, Family Medicine Education Consortium

I have worked with Family Physicians since 1978. After beginning my career as a family therapist and community organizer, I stumbled into a position as Director of Faculty Development and Behavioral Science at the Pennsylvania State University Department of Family and Community Medicine in Hershey PA.

I had not planned on spending the remainder of my career working in medicine and with Family Physicians. I joined the faculty with no understanding of medicine beyond what I experienced through TV and my personal experiences as a patient, which were thankfully very few. I was truly a neophyte.

What caused me to linger was the passion I discovered for what we now call patient-centered and relationship-centered health care. I came to see Family Physicians as the unsung heroes of medicine. It's not that they were the only ones who believed in the importance of a healing relationship. During my years in medicine, I have found many professionals across all medical specialties and the health care system who share a healer's vision for their work. Indeed, I believe that a community dedicated to healing can be found across the entire spectrum of helping professions.

What distinguishes Family Physicians from other occupations is that, in a world of reductionist thinking and action where people become patients and patient care becomes an opportunity to utilize high-tech skills, Family Physicians champion the generalist approach to care. At the heart of the generalist approach lies an understanding that health should not be viewed as a commodity, and healing is as likely to flow from a relationship with someone who can be trusted to stay with a patient no matter the problem as it is from performing a specialized procedure. As G. Gayle Stephens, MD one of the founders of Family Medicine said, "Family Medicine is primary care with soul."

The soul of medicine lies in a deep and abiding enthusiasm for establishing relationships with each person who seeks your care. The skill set required for a physician to develop relationships with individuals and families is challenging work. The physician must use a comprehensive approach that includes the biological, psychological, environmental and social issues in order to respond to those needs that can influence a patient's health and quality of life. At the core is a passion to serve and to stand with one's patients.

While Dan was in medical school at Penn State Hershey, Thomas Leaman, MD was the chair of the Department of Family and Community Medicine. Here is how Dr. Leaman expresses it:

> There is one principle that I think is absolutely basic to an understanding of what lies at the core of a Family Physician. That is the close, almost intimate relationship that develops between the family doctor and the patient. Attorneys shudder at the mention of actually hugging a patient; psychiatrists abhor the idea of touching a patient. Many family docs, with the patient's permission, occasionally pray with their patient. In my practice I learned, slowly, to love some of my most disagreeable (physically and morally) patients.

That relationship is truly one of the greatest therapeutic agents we have - it is most in evidence when we have nothing else to offer. It is also the source of one of the greatest joys of family practice.

In this book, Daniel Way displays a deep connection with his patients. He's the kind of person who drives by a house/trailer/ shack and wonders who lives there and why they live there. How do they make do? What is "the rest of their story"? This is an uncommon trait and reveals the heart, mind and soul of a Family Physician and even more importantly, a reverence for the human condition.

In *Never a Dull Moment*, the reader can step through the threshold of Dr. Way's gaze. His camera and his words speak volumes to those looking for a peek into the rest of the story about the people of the Adirondacks. These are tough minded, family oriented people who love their Adirondack ways.

I arrived at Penn State Hershey four years after Daniel Way became a Family Physician. I would have enjoyed the opportunity to know him as a student, though to be true, he still seems as full of curiosity and passion to explore the human condition as he must have been when the world of medicine was new to him. I have come to appreciate his quest to understand the people in his community through reading this book. I believe you will too.

Laurence Mahoney Bauer, MSW, MEd
Chief Executive Officer
Family Medicine Education Consortium
www.fmec.net

Gerald Merritt of Bigsby Pond, jazz enthusiast and Alzheimer patient.

INTRODUCTION

"What history needs more of is first-person testimony" – William Safire

Life is like a book. It has a beginning, it contains chapters, and it always has an ending. Practicing primary care medicine is like reading very interesting books. As a family physician, I follow the lives of my patients, chapter by chapter. Over time, I become a character in the books of their lives, while they become characters in the book of my life. I suppose it is only natural that some of their lives would become chapters in this book, and writing their stories is what keeps the book of my life endlessly fascinating. And just as life can be dramatic, humorous, heartbreaking and amazing, so I hope will be the true stories within these pages.

Practicing Family Medicine in the most rural area in the eastern United States for over thirty years has been a very rewarding experience for me. It's true that choosing that path meant placing myself in the lower end of the earnings bracket for my specialty, which is itself one of the least profitable fields in medicine. But my rewards, while less tangible, can't be bought with money. In the Adirondack hamlets of North Creek and Indian Lake in upstate New York, I have been able to experience the traditional role of town doctor, where I know almost everyone and almost everyone knows me. Most of my time is spent trying to prevent illness and death by treating patients' high blood pressure, diabetes, elevated cholesterol, substance abuse, or screening them for cancer and other common conditions. This may not seem very heroic or exciting because theoretically, if I do a perfect job, nothing happens. But along the way, I can socialize with my patients a little too. We can talk about mutual interests and our families, local news and world affairs. As a result, we often become friends, and then the levels of mutual trust, respect and affection can break down many of the modern-day barriers in the doctor-patient relationship. In a field of increasingly dehumanizing technology and bureaucracy, this

is worth more than money.

Over the course of my career I have witnessed the digitalization, hyperspecialization, over-regulation and dehumanization of medical care. In the early years I could see more patients every day and still get home two hours earlier than I do now. I have seen fellow physicians retire from the profession they used to love years earlier than they had planned after succumbing to compassion fatigue, the medical equivalent of battle fatigue. It is a sad irony that, while the miracles of medical research have enhanced the tools of my trade to an extent I would have thought impossible thirty years ago, the intrusion of the managed care and medical malpractice industries has created such a burden on physicians that, for many of us, the passion ignited in our youth for helping our fellow man has waned prematurely.

One of the sustaining forces that keeps me going is the relationship I have with my patients. Despite the many changes that have developed in the practice of medicine over the centuries for good or bad, that is the one constant which still attracts most primary care physicians to our profession. The opportunity to help thousands of individuals and families maintain or regain their mental and physical health means there will never be a dull moment in my day. My most enjoyable workday is the one or two days per month that I devote entirely to doing home visits throughout the southeastern Adirondacks. Seeing how and where my patients live, especially the elderly who may have been living in the same home for seventy or eighty years is sometimes the only way to appreciate how they function and survive. I can often learn more about the patient within thirty seconds of entering their home than in all of their previous visits to my office. My travels, which may exceed one hundred miles of driving in one day, also give me the opportunity to explore the most remote neighborhoods in the

On the summit of Algonquin Mountain, September 2009

Adirondack Park. Finally, my home visits allow me to use the other weapon I wield to combat compassion fatigue: my camera.

Many patients tease me about giving up my day job to become a professional photographer. I must admit that I have fantasized about the idea for most of my adult life. But I must also admit that for me, being an amateur rather than a professional photographer has its advantages. It's true I often curse my hectic work schedule and relative paucity of opportunities to go out and shoot the kind of images I see the pros take. Still, I can't escape the reality that my 'day job' as a physician, though not as defining of my identity as it is for many of my medical colleagues, remains a very rewarding and satisfying profession despite its many frustrations. My rural Adirondack medical career has defined my photographic career in ways that the pros cannot match. Without my patients and my familiarity with their surroundings, I would not be writing this book or displaying the photographs on its pages. So whenever a patient or colleague asks me if I would not rather be a full time photographer, I am reminded of a scene in the movie *Field of Dreams*. You know the scene where Ray Kinsella (Kevin Costner) reminisces with the elderly physician Archibald "Moonlight" Graham (Burt Lancaster) about his brief major league baseball career, which consisted of one-half inning.

"You came this close," said Ray to the old doctor. "It would kill some men to get this close to their dream and not touch it. They'd consider it a tragedy."

"Son," Graham replied. "If I had only been a doctor for five minutes, now that would have been a tragedy."

Fortunately, the two careers have fused together symbiotically. One of my favorite photographers, Margaret Bourke-White, once explained her passion this way:

What makes a photographer? An overpowering drive to show what he sees to the outside world.

Although landscape photography was what attracted me to this field of art, my day job has introduced me to the challenging genre of portrait photography in a way I could never have imagined when I joined the Hudson Headwaters Health Network in 1981. The proud and independent people of the Adirondacks are to me an endless source of wonder and admiration, whether they are a native whose family roots go back to colonial times or a retiree from Staten Island. For the most part, Adirondackers live here because they want to, because they like to, and that defines the common bond that makes them special. When I can write a story that describes the subject in the photograph and my relationship with him or her, it reinforces that special bond we have that attracted me to the profession in the first place. It also helps to offset the burden of bureaucracy and third-party meddling by insurance companies and government that threatens to depersonalize our relationship.

The history of American portrait photography includes many other examples of such work, going back as far as the photographs and essays by Jacob Riis, whose illustrated 1890 book *How the Other Half Lives* revealed in very personal terms the people and way of life of the tenement residents of New York City in the late nineteenth century.

Margaret Bourke-White published photographs of southern sharecroppers in her groundbreaking 1937 book *You Have Seen Their Faces*. Her future husband Erskine Caldwell, a journalist and author collaborated with her to produce a new type of book, as described by her biographer Vicky Goldberg:

You Have Seen Their Faces *established a new genre: a book in which photographs and text had equal weight. Although photographically illustrated books had long existed, the photographs themselves had always been secondary to the text... You Have Seen Their Faces welded photographs and literature together in a new balance.... A New York Times reviewer wrote that "The pictures produce such an effect, indeed, that...the text serves principally to illustrate them."*

Riis photo of tenement life in New York City

My own 2004 book *All In a Day's Work: Scenes and Stories from an Adirondack Medical Practice* was patterned after Bourke-White's, but it's subjects were the people I have had the privilege to take care of in my medical practice, as well as the beautiful Adirondack landscape in which they live. The uniqueness of the Adirondacks comes as much from its people as from its exquisite but challenging environment. What you will see in this book is a continuation of that dual theme. In looking at these photographs, many readers *will* have seen some of the faces and places on display in their own communities. Although most of the people I have included are my patients, I have also included a few colleagues, relatives and other Adirondack characters I have met along the way. Some are still here, while others have passed on since their stories were written. Their images and stories, however, remain alive, dated in the year when I created them. And their stories contain lessons they have taught me about life; lessons that I want to share with you, the reader. I hope you enjoy looking at and reading about these folks. You may have seen more beautiful images and read more fascinating stories elsewhere, but, like Bourke-White, I feel I must show this to the outside world. And like Jacob Riis, I feel it has merit. He justified his work this way:

> "The belief that every man's experience ought to be worth something to the community from which he drew it, no matter what that experience might be, made me begin this project."

I justify it another way: life is like a book, and I like to read. Come along and read with me…

Boyd Smith, Johnburg, October 1987

DEDICATION

Harriet Busch MD – Rural Primary Care Physician, Chester Health Center, October 2003

My wife Harriet Busch and I met in 1972 as fellow senior biology students at Penn State University who were trying to get into medical school. We found we shared a love for the Philadelphia Phillies, our Penn State Nittany Lions, and a desire to make something useful of our lives. She had already been accepted at Temple University's School of Medicine, while I would soon be accepted at Penn State's Hershey Medical School. For the next four years we racked up many miles traversing the Pennsylvania Turnpike, and in our fourth year we married and applied together for residencies in Family Medicine. Accepting three-year positions at Southside Hospital in Bay Shore, New York, our ultimate goal was to come back upstate to my hometown of Glens Falls, where we hoped to find a home and begin our lives as rural Family Physicians. Looking back after more than thirty years of living in a picturesque and wholesome community on the outskirts of one of the most scenic and best-preserved landscapes in the United States, we have been living the dream we had envisioned for ourselves those many years ago. Given the choice, we would probably do it all over again, but that doesn't mean it has been easy.

Having practiced rural primary care medicine in the Adirondacks for over three decades, I can attest to the demands and stresses it can cause, especially for my wife. Imagine that practice being based for a quarter century in the original health center of the Hudson Headwaters Health Network- a cold, drafty, cramped, outmoded building that featured a windowless physician's office no larger than a closet. Add to the burden the responsibility of being the *de facto* director of the health center, whose role is to make sure other providers' patients' problems get solved as well as her own. Now consider the responsibilities of successfully raising two children as a caring and dedicated mother, while maintaining an efficient and comfortable home. If you were to combine all these roles together into one person, you might think you were describing a saint. In this case however, I am describing my wife. Although she does have some saintly qualities, the first word I would use in describing her would be 'determined'. When it comes to getting a job done and doing it in a competent and tireless fashion, whatever it takes, even if it drains every ounce of energy she has left, there is no more reliable and determined person than Harriet Busch.

At times, Harriet reminds me of the wolverine. The wolverine is a compact but fierce mammal whose size often causes its adversaries to underestimate its ferocity and tenacity, especially when crossed. For example, when Harriet jogs or walks through the woods near our Glens Falls home, she is often tripped up or jumped on by unleashed and uncontrolled dogs, which are forbidden in the park. When she encounters the dogs' owner, she invariably confronts them with their transgression; no matter how much bigger or younger they are than she.

At other times she does remind me of a saint; specifically Saint Jude, the Patron Saint of Lost Causes. When she has a patient who is ill or has a crisis, she will spare no effort to resolve the problem. She will make phone calls on her day off to patients she is concerned about, make more phone calls to consultants before and after they have seen her patient, and basically do anything and everything she can for them. All she asks from her patients is that they cooperate. If the patient is sick enough to require hospitalization, Harriet will make sure that patient goes to the hospital. If they refuse, her identity can morph from Saint Jude back to the wolverine in a heartbeat!

More than once while on duty at Glens Falls Hospital I have received admissions from Harriet who said that the only reason they agreed to come to the hospital was because Doctor Busch had planted herself between themselves and the door, and they had no way to escape. One such patient was clearly sick and needed admission, but he was seriously thinking of signing out against medical advice. I had already explained why he could die if he went home, since he was acutely short of breath and hypoxic, had an abnormal EKG and was probably in congestive heart failure. If he left against medical advice he would probably die. That didn't sway him. "If I die, I die. So what?" I had to pull my trump card: "Then if you won't do it for yourself, do it for me. Can you imagine how angry Dr. Busch will be at me if she finds out I let you get away? Gimme a break!" He looked at me carefully, sizing me up and down like a fisherman eyeing a trout he had hooked, trying to decide whether to gut and fillet me or throw me back in the water. It seemed like he left me writhing on the hook for an eternity. Finally he declared, "You seem like a nice guy. I guess I'll stay!" Whew! As it turns out, he had triple vessel coronary artery disease including a 95% obstruction of his left anterior descending artery. His decision saved both our lives that day.

Dr. David Judkins, a cardiologist in Glens Falls who enjoys hunting and fishing in the Adirondacks, told me a typical Dr. Busch story. "I was deer hunting with a good friend of mine not that long ago, who is a real rough-and-tumble Adirondack kind of guy, always taking the hardest route through the woods and tough as nails. Our group was deep in the woods but after the first drive he said 'I have to go- I'll be back later.' When I asked him why he had to go he said he had a doctor's appointment. The rest of us gave him a hard time about scheduling a doctor's appointment during hunting season, but he said 'it's with Doctor Busch, and she'll kick my ass if I don't keep that appointment. Not many people can keep me on the straight and narrow, but I do what she says because I'm afraid not to. So I'll see you boys after my appointment!'"

Sadly, physicians like Harriet are an endangered species: the dedicated rural primary care physician. When Harriet and I were graduating from medical school, perhaps thirty percent of our fellow grads were choosing residencies in primary care (family medicine, pediatrics or internal medicine). When we joined Hudson Headwaters Health Network in the early 1980's, we had many applicants for every opening on our medical staff. The lure of practicing in northeastern New York with its beautiful landscapes, excellent recreational resources, and good school systems made it an irresistible destination for young practitioners looking for a place to settle down and raise a family. Not so much today. For most medical school graduates contemplating their career options, the lifestyle opportunities in rural areas such as the Adirondacks are often outweighed by the relatively lower income, just as primary care medicine cannot compete with the much higher wages of the medical specialties. As a result, family physicians are becoming a vanishing breed. In 2007, less than 2% of med school graduates were choosing rural primary care. Hopefully, the federal government's recent emphasis on promoting more cost-effective medical care will serve to give family medicine, pediatrics and rural medicine residencies the recognition and financial support they need to ensure that physicians like Harriet do not become historical footnotes.

Meanwhile, for over thirty years, Harriet had the determination to continue her work at the Chestertown-Horicon Health Center despite the long commute and the obstacles and frustrations of modern-day medicine. In 2005, she had the satisfaction of moving into the newly-built, state-of-the-art Chester-Horicon Health Center, now one of the nicest health centers in the network. As of 2012 she has relocated closer to home in the Queensbury Family Health Center, where she continues to tend to a very loyal and appreciative patient population. Some might consider Harriet's dedication to her patients saintly; certainly she has earned the respect of almost everyone she has worked with or taken care of. But she's no saint-she's 'just' a very competent, experienced rural primary care physician. That is why, for all she does and all she represents, this book is dedicated to Harriet Busch MD.

ADIRONDACK FOLKS

When the time comes that mankind, through overpopulation, environmental degradation, rising sea levels, resource depletion and loss of survival skills arrives at the brink of extinction, it might well be the people of the Adirondacks that emerge from our still-intact wilderness to carry on the species. Why? Because, while the increasingly urbanized citizens of our planet become better at exploiting the resources and infrastructure that our cities offer, they also become more dependent on them. Meanwhile, many Adirondackers can still survive in broken-down trailers and century-old cabins while living off the land without the electronic and digital support of the outside world, and be perfectly content to do so. For many Adirondack residents, visiting the nearest airport, train station, bus stop, grocery store, or mall is an all-day trip, while wi-fi and cell phone coverage is a pipe dream. What Adirondackers may lack in cultural sophistication and monetary wealth is compensated by retaining the ability to eke out an existence in a harsh environment that demands self-sufficiency. As the environmental author Bill McKibben wrote in his book *Wandering Home*,

Charles Davis, North Creek, April 2003

"The people of this territory are backward- which is to say that they're only a generation or two removed from knowing how to take care of themselves. Self-sufficiency remains a living memory...since almost no one (living in the Adirondacks) can make a living doing just one thing, the average Adirondacker has many more talents than the average American..... In my experience, the world contains no finer blend of soil and rock and water and forest than in this scene laid out before me.... And no place where the essential human skills- co-operation, husbandry, restraint- offer more possibility for competent and graceful inhabitation, for working out the answers that the planet is posing in this age of ecological pinch and social fray."

Like the Uygur people of central Asia, the Inuit of the Canadian arctic, or the Yanomamö of the Amazon rainforest, Adirondackers are well-adapted to their environment. Whether it be hunting, trapping and fishing; building, reusing and repairing; gardening and woodcutting, exploring and guiding, or simply earning a few bucks from scratch, the modern-day Adirondacker would be easily recognized by his/her ancestors of a century ago. They may not always live the healthiest of lifestyles, and they may develop some bad habits along the way. They usually have strong feelings and firm opinions about things, and don't much care if you agree with them or not. But in the event of an economic Armageddon, I have made it a point to keep a list of these multi-talented locals and be their best friend.

Of course, not everyone who lives in the Adirondacks has such skills, and some who once had them have lost them. They chose to live here anyway, just because they would rather live in these mountains than anywhere else. It may not be easy, and it may not always be fun, yet to regular Adirondack folks it is worth the hardship to be able to appreciate the natural landscape, wildlife outside the window, blazing starry skies, peace and quiet, community spirit, and knowing who your neighbors are. Here, the simple things in life like mountains, lakes and forest are still preferred to taxis, subways and concrete canyons. The following pages contain some examples of the Adirondack Folks I have met. You have been warned…

The Glen, Warrensburg

Eleanor and Albert Alger of Warrensburg

ALBERT & ELEANOR ALGER – ADIRONDACK SURVIVORS

Warrensburg, October 1989

Albert and Eleanor Alger were typical of the Adirondack population of their day. They were able to live happily on almost nothing, and they seemed totally devoted to each other. For years they lived along the Hudson River below The Glen, in a one-room cabin lit by a single 60-watt bulb and heated by an ancient wood stove. Eleanor had made a career as a circus performer, while Albert was once a lumberjack and woodcutter. They had very little income, and what little they had was spent on bare essentials – and lots of cigarettes.

When I made a house call on them in the early spring of 1989 to see how they had survived the winter, the temperature in the cabin must have been one hundred degrees. Being avid smokers, they were plagued by the consequences of their habit, suffering from emphysema, peripheral vascular disease and osteoporosis. When one of them was in the hospital, the other would somehow find a way to get down to Glens Falls to visit every day. This was despite the fact that, near the ends of their lives, neither one could drive. Relying on the kindness of neighbors and public health nurses, they took care of each other in their tiny home through years of debilitating illness. When I asked Eleanor how they survived with almost no visible means of support she replied lightheartedly, "We're not poor, we just don't have any money!"

When Albert's cardiovascular system finally succumbed to his tobacco addiction, Eleanor's powerful survival instincts were sorely tested. Having lived for so many years in that tiny bungalow overlooking the Hudson, it took over a year after Albert's death to convince her to move to a more supportive facility.

When her fragile support network finally collapsed, she reluctantly accepted nursing home placement. Once there however, she quickly adapted to the nurturing environment and became one of the staff's favorites. Their little bungalow no longer exists – another resourceful Adirondacker dismantled it and recycled or reused most of its materials.

The Alger's home

STELLA McARDLE
SOCIAL SECURITY RECIPIENT

North Creek, February 1988

Stella McArdle was a lucky lady. Although she developed Alzheimer's disease as a widow very late in life, she was able to live in the comfort of her own home despite her situation. Whenever I made a home visit, I would find her neatly dressed and well attended by a team of aides from the community who were hired by her son Edward to provide 24-hour care. Although most seniors in her condition would have spent their last years in our nearby nursing home, Stella's husband Jack had made Ed promise not to let that happen to his mother. Though he lived in The Bronx and had his own significant health problems, Ed kept the promise he made to his father at great personal cost in time, money and stress. When he came to North Creek to visit his mother, Ed would come into my office with her latest status report and a report of the great expense of providing her with private duty care. It wasn't until years after Stella's passing that I learned from Mary Moro, a friend of Ed's, how close Stella came to giving up her home due to a lack of personal savings.

"Stella was a real character!" Mary reflected. "She was the senior cafeteria worker at the Johnsburg Central School for many years, at a time when my daddy (Butler Cunningham, owner of the North Creek General Store) was the head of the school's board of education. In those days, paying into the Social Security Fund was optional in New York State, and for years, Stella refused to pay into it. Every time she came into the store, daddy would beg her to enroll. Finally, when she was in her late 50's, he forced her to sign up.

"As it turned out, she paid into Social Security for eight years before retiring, and she had no pension. Yet, she was able save most of that money and live out her life in her own home even after Jack died because of Social Security, and she lived for ninety-six years. It was the best deal of her life!

Stella McArdle, above. Hudson River near Stella's house, opposite.

Every time she saw me after she retired, she would say 'bless your father for what he did!'"

18

ANNA KOHRMAN & JAMES DANIELS – ADIRONDACK NEIGHBORS

Minerva, May 2000

Anyone who lives year-round in the Adirondack Park knows how unforgiving an environment it can be, especially to the elderly and disabled. There are no taxis, no public transportation, and once you are outside of the tiny hamlets and villages there are very few sidewalks or even neighborhoods in the modern sense. Houses are separated by snow banks, forests, mountains, and sometimes more intangible barriers such as the self-imposed isolation that many residents seem to relish. If you are in your nineties and living alone like Anna Kohrman, or disabled and unable to earn a decent living like James Daniels, it is especially difficult to survive. But Adirondackers are by nature a tough, individualistic, and resilient bunch, and both Jim and Anna are classic examples. In order to survive, they did what Adirondackers with seemingly nothing in common have been doing since the first settlers arrived here- they made friends.

A more unlikely duo than Anna Kohrman and Jimmy Daniels can hardly be imagined. Anna is a sassy, funny, outgoing, self-ridiculing, transplanted "flatlander" from Staten Island who, in a different life, could have been another Joan Rivers. Now in her late 90's, she has long-since outlived her husband Joe and her ability to function independently. Yet, her love for her adopted home in Minerva has forced her to endure the harsh winters and remoteness.

Jim is a very passionate, talented son of Japanese-American parents whose promising skills as a musician and master carpenter were forever compromised by a severe brain injury suffered in 1990 when he struck a deer while riding his motorcycle. His unusual injury has not only caused unpredictable and violent seizures, but also left him with the difficult combination of attention deficit, loss of impulse control, and a smoldering rage against the cruel circumstances that have left him almost penniless and unable to use his considerable abilities to earn the wages of a skilled craftsman. What was not taken from him, however, is his instinctive compassion and desire to help others, even though he needs others to help him. About the only thing Anna and Jim seemed to have in common was their birthday; they were both born on May 21st. As often happens, fate placed them in small bungalows on opposite sides of Fourteenth Road (I always wonder where the other thirteen roads are in Minerva, since there are none so named) in one of the prettiest and tiniest hamlets in southern Essex County. As I became involved first with Anna's health care, and then Jim's later on, I gradually came to appreciate their symbiotic relationship.

Anna explained to me that her transformation from a Staten Islander to a Minerva Adirondacker was not as great a leap as I imagined. "When Joe and I first bought our home in Staten Island for $7000 in the 1930's, it was farmland. It's hard to believe we once had fields and cows around us in Staten Island, but that's what it used to be like. My husband liked hunting in the Adirondacks, so we bought some land up here in Minerva to bring our kids to in the summer and fall. Back then, the land up here was more open than it is now- not so much different than Staten Island really." Over the years, as her downstate environment became engulfed by heavy development and urbanization, her Minerva neighborhood was being engulfed by the Adirondack forest, which was still rebounding from the heavy tree-cutting of the nineteenth century. As the two properties were becoming increasingly polarized, Anna and her husband found they preferred the Adirondacks. "One day in Staten Island we said 'That's it! We're getting out!' We sold our $7000 house for $137,000 and moved up here year-round."

By the time I met Anna, she was in her eighties and a widow. Rather than mellowing with age however, she had become increasingly peculiar, perhaps because of a combination of social isolation, the effects of aging, and her over-the-top sense of humor. A long-standing hearing problem characterized by partial hearing loss and ringing in the ears had evolved into a conviction that band music was playing in her head. The first time I remember seeing Anna, her chief complaint was "can you stop the music in my head?" She was convinced that the music was being picked up by the fillings in her teeth via nearby power lines or satellites! An MRI, EEG, complete hearing evaluation and consults with a neurologist, ENT specialist and a dentist failed to identify a cause. (Anna later admitted that the problem got much better when she told her neighbor to turn down his stereo!) Her capacity to drive was taken away by arthritis and dizzy spells, and friction with her children undermined much of their ability to lend her the support she needed, despite the best efforts of her granddaughter Corrine. When I asked her how she managed to get by, she would often credit her neighbor. "I don't know what I would do without Jimmy Daniels."

On one of my morning home visits with Anna, she consented to let me photograph her as she offered some coffee, cookies and doughnuts. Her zany, self-mocking humor was at its best as I set up my camera on a miniature tripod on the dining room table. "Can you get my brain in the picture? I'll try and look intelligent. Do you have a rogue's gallery? When you show this picture to people you can say 'See this lady? She took my medicine and lived 98 years!'" She had me laughing so hard I was having trouble setting up the camera. As I squeezed off the first couple frames, Jim Daniels arrived to look in on her as he so often did.

"Have a doughnut Jimmy!" she offered as he sat down beside her. I backed the camera up a few inches as Jim squeezed into the frame. Their banter continued as I tripped the shutter between bites of pastry. "When did that load of firewood arrive?" he asked, referring to the pile I had noted in her driveway when I arrived. "Yesterday afternoon, right after you left," she replied. Turning back to me she added, "I bought ten face cords for the stove- now I have to live long enough to burn it all…that is, if someone will stack it for me," casting a hopeful smile toward Jim. He laughed. "You know I will," he said tenderly, shaking his head in mock resignation.

Anna was more than happy to keep Jim busy with various projects, such as rebuilding her porch, for which she would pay him. It was a system that served her need for a man's help as well as his need for some pocket money to supplement his meager disability income. But there was more at work here; they clearly cared about each other. Anna was well aware of Jim's volatile temper and difficulty staying focused on tasks, but she saw past these traits. "I worry about Jimmy," she told me when he had left to tackle the woodpile outside. "I've known him since before his accident. He lost a lot from that but he's still a sweet boy inside. To me, he's a good friend, even though he could be a bad enemy. We get along pretty good. He helps me, and I help him." She shrugged then added, "That's what friends are for."

Hudson River Gorge near Anna's home

22

LOUIS MASTRO – PROFESSIONAL ARTIST

Warrensburg, August 2005

Although I have dedicated my professional life to the practice of medicine, there was a time in my youth as my high-school's yearbook photographer that I admit I did fantasize about becoming a professional cameraman for *National Geographic* magazine. Although I ultimately chose a different path (with no regrets, mind you), I have always had the greatest respect for those talented and brave souls who have the creativity and courage to pursue a full-time career in the arts. Artists are by nature passionate, consumed by their obsessive desire to produce works that reinforce their creative urges, often with relatively little emphasis on the marketability of their productions. Consumers of art are a finicky and unpredictable lot, who too often care more for the art than the artist and rarely appreciate the effort put into what they see. As a result, too many artists cannot make a living and must sacrifice their creative skills in exchange for a more secure and profitable livelihood. It is the rare artist indeed who has the combination of creative ability, productivity and marketing skills to make a living over a lifetime. Louis Mastro is one of those artists.

When Louis Mastro chose me as his physician in 2005, I acquired a patient who lived the life I might have wished for in some parallel universe. When I realized that he actually chose me because of my own interest in art, I felt I had found the best of both worlds. Here in my presence was a talented and successful artist whose professional history was so fascinating that it took me a while to remember that I was supposed to be focusing on his medical needs (fortunately he didn't seem to mind). His daughter Teresa Zappala, who accompanied him, briefly educated me about his background, beginning as a child in New York City where he was encouraged to pursue a career in the arts by his mother. While he learned to draw and paint at the Grand Central School of Art, the Leonardo DaVinci Art School, and the

Art Students League, his mother taught him to play classic guitar by ear. He also studied piano, violin, dance, and opera. As a young man he taught painting in Westchester County while becoming a member of the famed Salmagundi Club of Manhattan, where he rubbed shoulders with such renowned artists as Edward Hopper and took portraiture lessons from Walter Briggs. During the Second World War he used his artistic abilities to create diagrams for aircraft manuals and illustrate operational handbooks for all three branches of the military. After the war Louis used his commercial talents for more domestic markets, creating the Hersh-Mastro graphic arts studio in Manhattan where he enjoyed the patronage of major publishers and Madison Avenue advertising agencies. Meanwhile he was continuing both to teach art to his students and attend drawing classes himself. Working from 7 AM to 10 PM weekdays and 7 AM to 5 PM on weekends, his talent, portfolio and financial success all increased over the years, while his wife Sarah raised their two daughters and one son. The Mastros would vacation in such scenic places as the Atlantic coast, the Adirondacks, Florida, and the Caribbean, where Louis would paint and draw all day while Sarah and the children enjoyed their exotic surroundings.

By the 1950's, Mastro's success was recognized by President Eisenhower, who included Louis in his prestigious list of "Fifty American Artists". A decade later his children were grown and daughter Maria was on sabbatical in Portugal, during a time when the cost of living there was relatively modest. While visiting the Algarve region along the southernmost Portuguese coast with its exquisite scenery and architecture, Louis and Sarah found a lovely villa overlooking the Mediterranean and made it their winter home for the next twenty years. His creativity was energized to new levels, and his portfolio expanded with hundreds of new works over the years. By the time he and Sarah came back to New York his reputation had grown further, and he took advantage of this by opening successful galleries in Rockport Massachusetts and Fort Lauderdale which he continues to operate as of 2005. As if that were not a stimulating enough lifestyle, he also summered at his home in Warrensburg, hence his appearance in my North Creek office.

As I listened to him enthuse about his upcoming show opening at the Lower Adirondack Regional Arts Council gallery in Glens Falls, it took a while before I realized one other important fact: Louis Mastro was ninety-six years old! Here was a man who had the energy and enthusiasm of someone half his age, and the ambition to match. His most significant medical problem was a constant burning pain involving the entire upper right side of his head due to an attack of shingles that he had suffered twenty years before. Imagine having a migraine headache every day for two decades and you have some idea of the suffering this was causing him. I asked him how he could concentrate on his art when he is distracted by constant pain.

"It's the other way around," he replied. "I use art to distract myself from the pain. It gives me a way to relax and occupy my mind with pleasant and creative thoughts. Even when the pain awakens me in the middle of the night, I begin thinking of ideas for a new drawing or painting, or how I can improve something I'm working on. Sometimes I get so excited I

Louis at his LARAC opening

have to get up and work on it while the idea is fresh in my mind."

"It's true," Terri confirmed. "There hasn't been a day as far back as I can remember when he hasn't drawn or painted something, and when he's not doing that he's playing his guitar or listening to classical music."

I couldn't help thinking that if I could find a way to control his constant headache it would have a positive impact on his work and health. He left my office with a prescription for Carbatrol, and invited me to his show opening in Glens Falls the following week. After all I'd just learned about him, I was curious to see what more than eighty years of artistic experience looked like on canvas. Having grown up among a family of artists, I had great expectations.

On a warm August evening in 2005 I entered the Lapham Gallery of the Lower Adirondack Regional Arts Council in downtown Glens Falls to find a party in full swing. Louis was surrounded by an attentive crowd, clearly in his element. My first thought was "this is the first time I have attended a party for a ninety-six year-old which was not being held in a nursing home or hospital!" This thought was quickly forgotten as soon as my eyes began scanning the walls of the gallery. They were covered by a collection of watercolors, oils, and pastels that took my breath away. Not only were the individual works superb in their own right, but the range of method, medium and subject matter made the exhibit appear to have been created by an entire school of artists rather than an individual. In their execution it was clear that their creator was a master of fine art in the real sense of the word. The watercolors were detailed and exquisitely composed, the pastels were vibrant and the portraits were haunting. There were also abstracts that were provocative and inspirational. With prices for the paintings ranging from $2,400 to $10,000, this man was no amateur. Needless to say, I was impressed!

Working my way through the throngs of his admirers, I could see the pleasure and satisfaction on Louis' face as he talked about his work. He seemed happy to see me and accepted my praise magnanimously. I came away thinking that he was not only a master of fine art, but a master of aging. Terri was at his side and introduced me to her mother Sarah, whom I had heard so much about. Though quiet and unassuming, Terry assured me her mother was a lady of many abilities. "My mother has helped my dad stay alive and healthy through the years; she is one of his secrets to longevity. She loves to cook and has always been a health 'nut'… She entirely took care of the three of us, since my dad was a workaholic. She is a master seamstress. She made

Still-life of urinal in Louis' hospital room

It was no surprise to find him literally surrounded by his work in his studio where he was starting a new watercolor. He was clearly feeling better, and even his headaches were improving. Attempting to photograph him at his easel, I had to squeeze into the room, packed as it was with stacks of sketchbooks and dozens of unframed paintings leaning against the walls. Looking at Louis through my viewfinder, a new sense of wonder came over me as I watched him doing what he had been doing so well for three-quarters of a century. It brought to mind something William Lester Stevens, another artist from Rockport, Massachusetts, once said: "The wish to create is perhaps the strongest passion of human experience." If there was an explanation for Louis Mastro's productivity, that was it. In his own words, this is how Louis puts it:

"As I look back at my life, my paintings have helped me to relive that moment, capture that scene, feel the ocean breezes and clean fresh country air….all the beauties of nature, structures of man, curves and magnificence of the human body, preserved for myself and for posterity….that is my purpose for painting. Art is my life. It pleasantly consumes my waking hours, and gives me peace, relaxation and a sense of accomplishment."

We should all be so fortunate- but then, we would all have to have the ambition, self-discipline, imagination and raw talent possessed by Louis Mastro.

our clothing, from pocket books and matching hats & coats, to formal dresses and costumes. Meanwhile she has been presidents of the PTA, Women's Clubs, Garden Clubs, and she has a magical green thumb too. Sarah also supported our dad in his artistic endeavors and adventures around the world…. Behind every 'Superman' is a 'Super Woman'!" The Mastros' sixty-eight-year relationship was living proof that a successful and stable marriage did indeed enhance both the quality and quantity of life.

Not long after that special evening, Louis developed a nasty cough which soon landed him in Glens Falls Hospital with pneumonia. Although this can be a life-threatening illness in a man his age, he seemed to fight it well, amazing all the physicians and nurses who took care of him. While most patients his age would be passively lying in bed during their stay, Louis used every free minute drawing and sketching everything in his environment, from the nurses and family visitors to the landscapes outside his window. Showing me his sketchbook, my eye was drawn to one still-life in particular. The objects looked familiar enough, but I couldn't help wondering if this was the first time in the history of art that an artist had sketched a urinal!

He left the hospital within a few days and I arranged a home visit soon thereafter to see if his recovery was continuing at home. Naturally, I brought my cameras.

At his Warrensburg home with Sarah

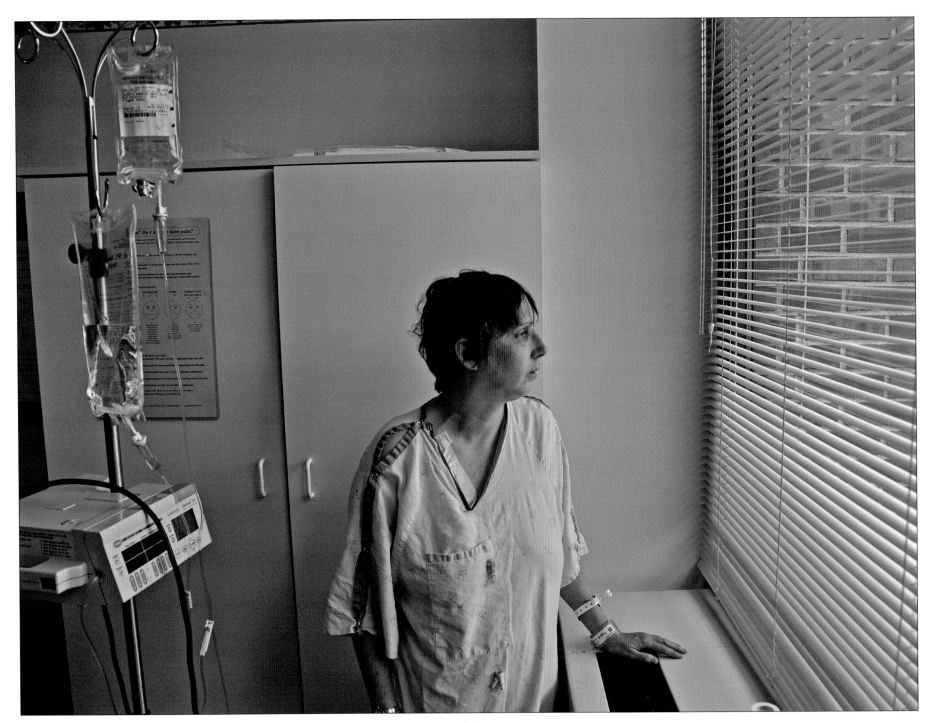

DARLENE STOWELL – MITOCHONDRIAL DISEASE PATIENT

Glens Falls Hospital, May 2009

Treating patients with chronic pain is one of the most common and challenging problems primary care physicians face. Pain is an incredibly complex issue, given its myriad causes, patterns, types, and patient responses to it. When the cause of the pain is known, such as when a patient has suffered trauma, or has a disease such as cancer or arthritis, it allows patient and physician to focus on the prognosis and most appropriate treatment. But when one's pain seems to be purely subjective, because its source cannot be revealed by blood tests, x-rays, or MRIs, it becomes much more difficult to deal with for both parties. All too often, the patient is assumed to be exaggerating or even inventing the pain, sometimes with justification. For those whose pain is real but unexplainable, the pain itself is often less difficult to bear than the implication from family, friends and health care providers that they are malingering or seeking narcotics to abuse, sell, or both. Ask Darlene Stowell – she knows about pain.

Benjamin Franklin once said "There are no gains without pains." If the corollary was that 'there are gains with all pains', then Darlene would be a very fortunate woman, for she has experienced more than her share of pains in her life. In fact, it is hard for her to remember the last time she was *not* in pain. Unfortunately, she has gained very little from it, and has lost much of what we all take for granted- freedom of movement, self-sufficiency, and feeling rested after a good night's sleep. "I remember in grade school falling asleep during class," she told me in November 2012, "and awakening to being yelled at by the teacher who would say 'Don't you go to bed early enough? Are we boring you?'" What made the pain even harder to bear for most of her life was that she did not know the cause, and no medical providers had a satisfactory explanation. "Pain was always there, and even as a little kid I tried to push myself into doing the same

things the other kids and my siblings were doing and it would only cause more pain that I couldn't explain."

When I first met Darlene, she was a 45-year-old woman whose pain had been attributed to fibromyalgia (FM), a mysterious disease which usually affects women in their thirties to fifties and is characterized by chronic aching pains in the muscles and ligaments that can extend almost from head to toe. It is worsened by physical activity, bad weather and inadequate sleep. I have had many such patients over the years, and have usually found that with proper patient education and adequate lifestyle changes, including weight loss, a graduated increase in conditioning exercises, not smoking, and using non-habituating medications to ensure adequate sleep, the patient can become more comfortable and enjoy a reasonably good quality of life. Some can even become well enough to enjoy skiing, hiking, swimming and other recreational activities with an acceptable degree of discomfort, although they always require more rest and have less endurance that their peers.

Darlene had all these symptoms and seemed to meet the diagnostic criteria for FM, except that her degree of pain and disability seemed far beyond what would be expected with the disorder. When she constantly seemed to be requiring more pain medication and spending more time in the emergency room at Glens Falls Hospital, she was considered a "drug-seeker." Eventually it became obvious that something more serious was at work in her case- but what?

When Darlene became a patient at the North Creek Health Center, her symptoms seemed too dramatic and varied to fit the FM stereotype, and childhood onset was very atypical. She told me the symptoms made her feel stupid and sick: "I was born with a learning disability, and by the time I was 14, I had failed first, second, and fourth grade, with no answer to why I had so many problems with learning, because when I would study my spelling homework, I would do good at home, but by the next day I couldn't remember how to spell the words… Every day was gastrointestinal problems so bad that I couldn't go to the bathroom without doubling over with constant painful spasms in my stomach, for days on end. By the time I was eighteen I never told the doctors, or my parents, because I was so darn embarrassed by it." And then there was the muscle pain- ever present, especially with any physical exertion: "…as a kid, I could never explain why, when my family played kickball, climbed a small hill to sled, or any sport in school and any other running around games, I became tired and would stop doing it after a few times. I would sit and watch and be called a wimp and lazy and no fun…Words hurt when you are a kid and I never could tell anyone including my own family why."

Finally, in January 2009 my colleague Dr. Jim Hicks referred Darlene to Dr. Darius Adams at the Albany Medical Center to be tested for genetic diseases. A muscle biopsy revealed Complex 4 Deficiency, one of the more common forms of mitochondrial disease. At last, the cause of Darlene's pain and suffering had a name; but the news was not good- there was presently no effective treatment, and there is no cure. Even so Darlene remembers, "I was, like, relieved that I wasn't going crazy; I wasn't imagining it after all. For years I had been told I was bipolar, a hypochondriac, had tennis elbow, spastic colon, fibromyalgia, personality disorder, or they just didn't know. At the same time, it left me angry – *very angry* – at my family, the doctors; everybody who kept saying to me 'get over it', 'deal with it'. It took me a long time to get over the anger."

Mitochondria are the tiny furnaces in every cell of our bodies, whose job is to turn fuel into the energy required to keep us alive and functioning normally. A complex series of enzymes normally work like an assembly line to turn the fuel (glucose) into energy and its byproducts (adenosine triphosphate, carbon dioxide and water). A mutation in any one of those enzymes can create havoc in that assembly line, causing useless or toxic metabolic byproducts such as lactic acid to build up in one's tissues. The brain, muscles and gut, which have the greatest need for energy, suffer the most. Research has begun to reveal the true extent of mitochondrial syndromes, and it is a scary situation. According to Edison Pharmaceuticals, a company that is involved in that research,

Inherited mitochondrial diseases are genetic disorders that share as a common link defects in how cells make and regulate energy… An estimated 2,000 defects in nuclear DNA and 200 defects in mitochondrial DNA have been identified as pathogenic…The incidence of mitochondrial disease is estimated at 1:10,000. However, this number may underestimate the true number of people with mitochondrial disease… Some estimates place the clinically diagnosed mitochondrial disease patients without a genetic diagnosis- so-called mitochondrial syndromes- at 10 times the incidence of genetically defined disease.

My own belief is that fibromyalgia is a mild form of mitochondrial syndrome.

These days, Darlene spends a lot of time in the Glens Falls Hospital emergency department due to flare-ups of muscle and abdominal pain, nausea and vomiting, and severe weakness. The best the ER doctors can do is infuse her with intravenous hydration, antiemetics and narcotics, and if she requires admission she is usually sent to the oncology floor where it is quiet. "The rest in a quiet room works really well," she says. "They also have a free massage therapist there and massaging my sore muscles really helps a lot." She now has an indwelling IV catheter to administer hydration and pain medications at home, but there are times when she still feels so badly she can't stand it. She has tried standard therapies such as high doses of oral coenzyme Q-10 and intravenous L-carnitine infusions, but as with most patients, these treatments have proven useless. The most effective drug to date in relieving her most acute symptoms has been oral dronabinol, a synthetic version of THC, the active ingredient in marijuana. Ironically, although the drug has given her relief of both pain and nausea in the hospital on several occasions, I cannot prescribe it for her as an outpatient since the FDA has only approved it for use in patients receiving cancer chemotherapy. At the present time, Darlene and I are hanging our hopes that new treatments, such as those being tested by drug companies like Edison, will have some impact in allowing 'mito' patients to live their lives without the near-constant pain and weakness that make it so difficult to get out of bed every morning.

Meanwhile, Darlene has learned how to cope with mito the best she can. "I have to plan around the weather forecast," she says. "Cold weather, especially if it is also damp or humid, makes a huge difference in how I feel. A temperature of around seventy degrees is perfect for people with mito. Sunny days make me feel very happy, although too much direct sun is bad for mito too. What about the pain, I ask. "Don't live in the pain," she replies decisively. "I have my bad days, and I have my good days. When I'm having a bad day, I think about my good days. You have to do that because if you dwell in the pain every day it's going to destroy you. So you have to make the best of the good days. If I'm having a good day I'll do something that will put a smile on my face. If it's sunny out I can get out and do something, even if I pay for it for the next three or four days- it's definitely worth it. Phil (Darlene's partner) will take me out for a little hike, or drive me somewhere. It doesn't have to be a big thing. I enjoy taking pictures, like you!"

I asked Darlene about her long-term goals. "It's kind of hard to have long term goals when you don't know from one day to the next if you can function," she answered. "I have to live day-to-day." She pauses. "I want you to tell my story to others who have symptoms like mine so they can get checked for mito. It's better to know than to be treated like a drug-seeking hypochondriac. In all reality I want to be a cadaver body when I die. Maybe it'll help scientists learn something more about the mito."

I have learned a lot from Darlene- no doubt more than she has learned from me. She taught me that a person can cope with a terrible disease and still experience some happiness. Patients such as Darlene keep me humble.

Moxham Mountain near Darlene's home

MARY FUNFGELD – COOKIE-MAKER EXTRAORDINAIRE

Warrensburg, December 2002

My job would be a great deal easier if more of my patients were like Mary Funfgeld. Mary is a physician's dream patient. She doesn't smoke, doesn't drink, and she gets a lot of exercise. She is active in her community and has a supportive family. And even at seventy-five Mary can still fit into a pair of blue jeans. She is generally healthy and takes good care of herself. She doesn't need to take very many medications, so I don't have to order many blood tests, x-rays or scans on her. When she comes to see me about her occasional headaches or arthritis pains, we can usually cover all the necessary medical topics within two minutes. Because of that, I get to spend a few extra minutes just 'visiting' with her and learning more about her as a person. That is how I have learned what has made Mary the kind and generous human being she truly is, and what often makes the difference between a happy, well adjusted individual and one who has to struggle through life just to find peace of mind. Mary was apparently the beneficiary of excellent parenting from an extended family, and she is justifiably proud of her heritage.

"When my mother was eighteen in the early 1900's, my grandfather John Henry Lewis brought his family to the United States from Seven Sisters, a little village near Swansea in southern Wales to buy some coal mines in Forest City, Pennsylvania," Mary explained. "He had bushy eyebrows and a big moustache. He spoiled his grandchildren rotten!" However Mary's mother, named Mary Elizabeth Evans, made sure her daughter grew up with a proper work ethic.

"My mother was proud of her roots. The Welsh were poor people but honest, honorable, religious and strong. And she passed that pride along to me. She taught me that in America, you can get whatever you want if you work hard enough for it. 'Hard work never killed anybody' she always

said, and when she said something, that was it. That's the way we were brought up, and that's the way it should be." By the time the younger Mary was eighteen, her mother's yearning for her native land drew her back to Wales, where she lived the rest of her life, leaving Mary to become the independent and assertive woman she remains today.

Mary put her mother's advice to good use developing a career in the restaurant business, working her way up the ladder in the Howard Johnson's Corporation out of Westbury Connecticut while raising a family that eventually included three sons. By the time they were grown, she had divorced, and she grew restless. "A friend of mine lived up here and said I would like it here in the Adirondacks. So in 1976 I put my life savings of five hundred dollars into a three-acre lot on Trout Lake and worked like a dog to save enough to build a house on it." After living on the lake for over ten years, she sold the property and moved to an unpretentious but comfortable ranch home in Warrensburg. "I like to keep things simple. The Warrensburg home was a lot easier to take care of, and I wasn't getting any younger." Classic Mary Funfgeld.

Another thing Mary's mother taught her was how to make cookies. "She was taught the recipe by her grandmother, and she taught it to me when I was a little girl. I've been baking my great-grandmother's cookies for sixty-five years now, and it makes me happy that I can share them with the people I care about in my life. The best thing my mother ever left me were her English baking sheets. They're paper-thin, so they never burn the cookies. That's why, even when people use my great-grandmother's recipe, they come back telling me mine taste better." Years ago, Mary began giving away her cookies in large tins and jars to her friends. My office at the North Creek Health Center has been honored to be included on her cookie list, and my staff and I have become part of the annual tradition of collecting, saving and returning cookie cans and jars for Mary to reuse the following year. As time has passed, it seems that Mary just works harder to provide the seasonal treats to the family, friends, neighbors, postal workers, fellow parishioners, doctors, and countless others on her expanding list. She begins buying supplies in November, including over twenty pounds of butter, carloads of flour, sugar and walnuts. Baking begins before Thanksgiving and for the next month she is basically a cookie-making machine. "It's a tradition," she explains. "Now everybody counts on me, so I don't want to let them down."

After being the grateful recipient of her generosity for many years, I wanted to see her in action at crunch time- when she begins her annual baking marathon in her cozy Warrensburg home. I was met in the front yard by her constant companion, a friendly Sheltie dog with a very intelligent face. "Hello, Spike," I said, recognizing him from the many photos Mary had shown me during her visits to my office. Sensing that I was a welcome guest, Spike stepped aside without barking or challenging me as I met Mary at the front door. "Spike is my best friend," she said with obvious affection. "We do everything together. He even helps me make the cookies!" Assuming she spoke metaphorically, I got a quick tour of her home and set up my camera as she began making another batch of her famous goodies. Every surface in the kitchen was piled high with cookie tins, and a familiar sweet aroma filled the room. I didn't have to ask why she went to all this trouble every holiday season. "I can still hear my mother's voice and feel her next to me when I'm baking," she said wistfully. "She taught me that the one thing that really matters is L-O-V-E, and whatever God gives you, that's life. You take what He gives you, and always keep the faith. Believe that things will work out- maybe not the way you planned, but everything will turn out okay. You can take anything you want from me, but you can't take away my faith: never ever. Every morning that I wake up and I can walk, I can see, with a roof over my head and food on the table I give thanks. What more do I want? There's nothing else, 'cause you can't take anything with you to the next life. My mother taught me that, and I instilled it in my three boys. I may not have many riches, but I can honestly say that I'm the richest woman in Warrensburg."

As Mary philosophized, her hands were in constant motion measuring, pouring, mixing, kneading, with Spike and I watching her every move. She recounted recent visits to her son's homes in New Jersey and Long Is-

Spike, the Wonder Dog

34

land where she enjoyed frolicking with her seven grandchildren. Gradually I realized why, at 75, she looked and acted ten years younger. Her mother's gift of self-esteem suffused Mary with the belief that she could survive any challenge. Her altruism gave her the desire to share her passion for life with others. Mary's love for her sons' families kept her connected with grandchildren who doted on her. A respect for her heritage compelled her to pass along an appreciation for her great-grandmother's recipe, which kept her very busy collecting the containers, purchasing the supplies, then baking and distributing the finished product. Her life still had purpose and structure, yet was simple and uncluttered by material things or time concerns. "I don't want no answering machine!" she said pointedly. "If you don't get me, call me back later!"

I left Mary's house impressed by her energy, passion, faith and generosity. Driving home munching on one of her still-warm creations, I anticipated the pleasure of giving Mary an enlargement of the touching photo I had taken of her with Spike, which clearly showed the bond between them. They seemed soul mates, able to communicate wordlessly. Just then, as I reached for another cookie, I noticed a small brown hair on its surface. Knowing Mary's hair to be white, I could only conclude it belonged to Spike. Was Mary's claim that he helped make the cookies more than metaphorical? Was he really that smart????

….Naaaah.

Schroon River in Warrensburg near Mary's home

DAN MOORE & ED BENNETT – ADIRONDACK LOGGERS

Indian Lake, October 2005

Any student of Adirondack history knows that the protective respect which many New Yorkers feel for our forest has not always been present. Ever since the Royal Navy of King George III took a fancy to the towering white pines that became the masts of His Majesty's British fleet in the late 18th century, the trees of the Adirondack forest have been the region's most important and enduring commodity, and for the next century, little thought was given to their aesthetic value. As the Native American tribes yielded their homeland to white settlers, they witnessed the conversion of their woods into charcoal to fuel the smelters of early Adirondack iron mines, while tanneries clear-cut huge tracts of forest merely for the tannins in their bark. The paper and lumber industries escalated the deforestation further so that, by the late 19th century, huge swaths of the Adirondacks laid barren and scarred. It is only due to the foresighted efforts of early environmentalists such as Seneca Ray Stoddard and Verplank Colvin that the Adirondack forest was saved from oblivion over a century ago. Even today, Stoddard's images of "drowned lands" and acres of stumps remain a cautionary visual tale, while modern day battles to stop the clear-cutting of old-growth trees of the tropical rain forests, Alaska and the Pacific Northwest often make practitioners of the arcane field of tree-harvesting appear to be no more than money-hungry brutes who care nothing for the forest itself. I have to admit that, having years ago seen Robert Glenn Ketchum's powerful photographs expose the despoiling effects of clear-cutting on Alaska's old-growth Tongass Wilderness, I was convinced logging in the Adirondacks must be bad too. As a rural physician practicing in the hamlets of Indian Lake and North Creek,

nestled within the beautifully intact forest of the Adirondack Park, I had little respect for the lumbermen who came into my office or the hospital with injuries ranging from bruises, lacerations and strained backs to crushed skulls and mangled limbs. It took years for me to appreciate that the logging industry might actually be an important reason why the forests have survived, and that there were reasons having nothing to do with money which led men (and occasionally women) to choose such a career. Patients Dan Moore and Edwin Bennett helped me appreciate and respect their way of life.

Dan and Ed, both of Indian Lake, are as true a pair of Adirondackers as you will ever meet. Anyone who is familiar with their town will recognize the names. In addition to the twenty-eight Bennetts listed in the Indian Lake phone book, there is a Bennett road right off Main Street near the fire station. The Moore name is not far behind with eighteen entries in the directory, and Dan's family has been involved with the running of the local post office, school board, real estate and wood products industries. Both men were destined to work in the woods. For one thing, they live in Hamilton County, which sports the lowest population density of any county east of the Mississippi and is essentially an unbroken blanket of trees (punctuated with thousands of lakes and ponds). Other than the local highway, government, school and seasonal tourism jobs, there isn't a lot else. Logging is considered a vital part of the local economy, as a bumper sticker commonly seen in Hamilton County points out in a typically Adirondack way: "If you object to logging, try using plastic toilet paper." Dan's father Richard ('Rip' to his friends) started his Indian Lake logging business in the 1950's, and Dan was already helping his dad in the forest when he was seven. "After high school," he told me, "I tried

Dan Moore and Edwin Bennett

building houses for a contractor, then I built a few myself, including my own home. But it was just a matter of time before I joined my father's business. Once it's in your blood you can't get it out. You have to have done it to appreciate it."

I guess that was my problem- my experience with logging was limited to what happens when things go wrong. In fact, as a young physician just out of residency in 1981, the first fatal accident I saw was an elderly woodsman whose skull was crushed by a "widow maker," a huge tree branch that had fallen on him as he was cutting the trunk. Another patient of mine is disabled by a brain injury and resultant seizure disorder suffered under similar circumstances. I knew that Ed Bennett's previous employer was also killed by a tree that he brought down on himself in 2002. Wondering whether Hamilton County lumberjacks were merely clumsier than their brethren elsewhere, I Googled the US Department of Labor's data on the hazards of logging operations nationally, and was amazed to learn that cutting trees for a living was far more dangerous than being a member of the US Army in Iraq. According to the Occupational Safety and Health Administration,

The 1992 Census of Fatal Occupational Injuries, a public report compiled by the Bureau of Labor Statistics (BLS), indicated that there were 158 fatalities in the logging industry, which amounts to a 2 in 1000 risk of death each year. The National Institute of Occupational Safety and Health (NIOSH) estimates that there are 16,500 compensable injuries each year in the logging industry. This amounts to an incidence rate of 1 in every 5 loggers. According to the US Department of Agriculture (USDA), the accident rate in the logging industry has pushed workmen's compensation insurance to 40 percent of payroll costs. The USDA estimates that this now amounts to over $90 million annually in the Pacific Northwest Region alone. According to a study conducted by the BLS, at least 47 percent of all injuries reported occurred in non-pulpwood logging operations.

Knowing this, I pressed Dan to explain what he enjoys most about his work and how he limits the risks of injury to himself and Ed. "I like not having to answer to anyone," he answered. "You know what I mean. You're out in the woods all day. That's why ninety percent of us do it. We like

the forest. I've never suffered a serious injury myself, though I know people who have. It's all about how you go about your work. If as boss I push people so hard they don't watch what they're doing, they'll get hurt. If you back off a little bit and get them time to think, they're better off."

I admitted feeling a sense of irony- as an admirer of the forest myself, it was hard to imagine that someone who cuts trees down all day could appreciate the woods as something other than a source of income. The more I talked to Dan and Ed the more I came to understand that they appreciate the forest as much as I do and understand it a lot better. That's why, when Dan invited me to spend an afternoon with them on the job in the winter of 2004-5, I jumped at the chance. I had just gotten a Nikon D-70, my first digital SLR camera, and I was eager to see what it could do. We agreed that on my next Wednesday afternoon off after completing a tour of duty at Glens Falls Hospital I would drive to the home of Dan's mother Lorraine (Rip had passed away a few years earlier) where Ed would meet me with his heavy-duty pick-up and drive me deep into the forest between North River and Indian Lake. They had been cutting veneer wood (hardwood for building furniture and paneling) for the past two winters on a privately-owned hundred-acre lot which abuts forest owned by Finch, Pruyn Corporation of Glens Falls, one of the oldest privately-owned paper companies in the United States. When the day came in late January 2005 for me to enter their world, about ten inches of new snow from the night before covered the forest with a deep but fluffy mantle of light powder. Although there was no wind, the temperature was only about ten degrees above zero, and a lazy, silent snowfall was adding to what was already on the ground. The sounds we were making as we drove deeper into the wilderness were the only ones for miles around. As Ed, who bears more than a passing resemblance to Nick Nolte, drove slowly along the bumpy logging road, we talked about his work.

"I love what we do," he said. "Where else can you have a job where you don't have to put up with paperwork, bosses and time clocks? Dan is my boss, but we're more like a team. And instead of walls we got great landscapes, sunrises and sunsets, and unbelievable wildlife. Deer, owls, foxes, coyotes, eagles- even timber wolves." Sensing my surprise he added "Oh yeah, we definitely have wolves in the Adirondacks- I've seen a few- they are a beautiful animal. I remember one day a coyote sat next to me

Dan Moore

twelve-foot logs with the slasher saw. Ed got to work fixing a chain on the skidder tire that had broken that morning. As I looked beyond the mound of logs that encircled the clearing, I was struck by how well the surrounding forest looked, considering the time they had already spent harvesting the lot- this was no Tsongass clear-cut. I mentioned this to Dan as he greeted me. "You've gotta do it right so the forest can keep on going. That's number one with us."

"Do all loggers feel that way?" I asked. He shook his head. "Some loggers have trouble protecting the forest because they own a couple million dollars worth of equipment, so they can't stop cutting when it's raining, and that's hard on the land. If Ed and I hit a rainy day, we just don't come out here, so we don't mess things up in the woods. Other one- and two-man crews usually feel the same way, but then you've got bigger crews with so much invested in machines and salaries that they can't stop, and that can be hard on the forest. Big crews mostly work for paper companies and big land owners. They've got the big tracts of land, so we don't compete with them. We take the smaller lots- maybe a few hundred acres, and Ed and I end up making more money apiece than the big crews."

At that point I shut up and let the men do their work. Ed spent half an hour under the skidder on the chain repair before riding it like a huge steel buffalo deeper into the woods. I concentrated on watching Dan operate the hydraulic claw on his truck as he lifted one log after another onto the back of his truck. I was impressed by the ease and dexterity with which he guided the mechanical arm up and down, back and forth as though it were prosthetically attached to his body, fitting the wood precisely onto the truck crib. Partly in an attempt to keep warm I clambered up onto the top of the truck to photograph him at the controls while flakes of snow gathered on his hat and shoulders. A few minutes later, as my fingers began getting numb from the cold, I almost lost my grip on the side of the truck on my way back down. The slip made me appreciate how easy it would

all afternoon, like he was looking out for me." As their workplace appeared ahead with Dan's log truck and trailer, skidder, slasher saw, and mobile work shed, I couldn't help observing "You and Dan must have to spend a lot of time working on your equipment!"

"You can't believe it," Ed acknowledged. "He's got a 1978 skidder- if that goes, a new one costs maybe $250,000. A new truck is over $125,000. Dan takes real good care of what he's got. That skidder can do anything a new one can, except the new ones have enclosed cabs with heaters. Who the hell wants to climb in and out of that heat?" he said with disdain. "I like the cold!" he added, lighting a Marlboro for emphasis at the thought. Somewhere else I would have said something about his smoking, but I was on his turf today.

We got out of Ed's truck to find Dan cutting recently felled trees into

Edwin Bennett with skidder

Finally, as the setting sun dropped below the treetops, the men called it a day and began preparing for the ride out. They secured the logs onto the truck using long, thick fabric straps that unrolled from spools up and across the top of the crib, down the other side and winched tightly onto another spool using steel bars as levers. I climbed into the forest-green log truck with Dan and we headed back to civilization. Looking out at the sylvan landscape, I asked him how he knows where the boundaries are between private and state land, and how easy would it be to simply sneak into the vast state-owned forest and grab a few trees. He didn't hesitate.

"Some areas are policed more carefully than others, but around here if you log on state land you're pretty much gonna get caught. Greg George (the state forest ranger) will see to that. I work real close with him-the lot we are on now borders state land, and before I even made a road through it I notified him. Then when I cut the road in Greg came and we took a walk together. He 'painted the line' along the border (marking trees with a spot of paint) and found that the owners had twenty-five more acres than I thought because of an old boundary dispute that they had won against the state. Greg's honest and he's there, so cheating is not an option."

"I think loggers invented the term 'mud season'," Dan said. "In the early spring we are out cutting trees for firewood (so buyers can have time to cut, split and dry the wood for the next winter) until the ground thaws, then we get out of the woods for a while. That's when I do a lot of mechanical work, fixing up my equipment and looking for new wood lots. Every logger in New York State has to be certified every two years, so if we have to go to school, we do it in the spring. We take classes at the DEC and Forestry offices on Warrensburg and Potsdam learning CPR, forestry

be to suffer a fall, or lose control of a chainsaw for a split second, a mistake that could take a limb or a life. A look at Ed's hands as he re-emerged from the woods later revealed the effects of a few such mishaps. (A couple months later would find him in my Indian Lake treatment room where I sewed up a small laceration that could have easily cost him his big toe had the saw cut just a half-inch further into his boot top.) As I attempted to warm my own hands, I asked him if the cold ever became a limiting factor in their work.

"Oh yeah, pretty much nothing works if it's ten below or less. That's where we draw the line." Realizing that it was twenty degrees warmer than that at the moment, I sucked it up and stuffed my hands under my armpits.

law, bookkeeping skills and so on. Tree cutting begins in late spring when things are a little drier and runs all the way through summer to the hunting season in fall. Lots of us hunt, and being out in the woods for a living gives us an advantage when it comes to knowing where the game is. That's also when the other rainy season is, so we wait until winter freezes the ground before we go back and do our skidding."

As a photographer and lover of the outdoors, I also appreciate the different seasons, but apart from the flu season and the driving challenges, there isn't much of a cycle to my work. For all its challenges, satisfaction and rewards, the physician's workday can get pretty tedious and confining. As we bounced along the road that Dan had built himself, I was reminded of how Bill McKibben described Real Adirondackers (see introduction). By McKibben's definition, Dan and Ed are Real Adirondackers, I thought as I looked out the windows at the forest surrounding us. It finally sank in that this private land had remained undeveloped and was producing revenue for the local economy because individual investors and companies like Finch, Pruyn hold onto it for its valuable timber. Once Dan is done harvesting it, these woods might remain untainted by man for another twenty or thirty years. Meanwhile, the deer, turkey and their predators (perhaps including the wolf) can flourish in the opened areas until a new generation of trees fills the breeches, when another generation of loggers would return to repeat the cycle. At least, I found myself hoping so. With all the intense pressure to expand the second home market in wild areas, I would far rather see Dan's successors here in a quarter century than a wall of condominiums. I could better appreciate

the risks he and Ed took but also the rewards of interacting with the forest on a daily basis. As a doe and a four-point buck curiously watched us pass their vantage point in a stand of cedar, I almost wished I could join them again the next day. But although I would instead return to my world of science and medicine, I could take comfort from the realization that all the logging trucks I see plying the highways from the Adirondacks to the mills in Glens Falls and the veneer markets in Canada was a healthy sign that, perhaps in a hundred years, this special place we call the Adirondacks might not look very different than it does today.

Securing the wood

FRED & LARETA STEWART – LOVEBIRDS FOR OVER 70 YEARS

Bakers Mills, May 2005

When it comes to the human appearance, most people feel that physical beauty diminishes with age. If that is true, then Fred and Lareta Stewart must have been a hot-looking pair when they first met over seventy years ago, because they are still regarded by everyone in Bakers Mills as the most attractive couple in town. And when you get to know them as I have over a quarter-century, you realize that their beauty is far more than skin-deep. Although they have lived most of their lives in their tiny Adirondack hamlet, their graceful manners and mutual respect lend them an uncommonly sophisticated elegance given their simple and rustic environment.

"I met Rita when I was seventeen years old," Fred told me one spring morning in 2005. I was visiting him to check on his progress as he recovered from a fractured right femur suffered the preceding winter. Knowing how close they were, I was curious how Fred and Rita had first met. "In those days," he reflected, "everyone knew everyone else. I lived in Sodom then, and I would walk to Bakers Mills at night with no flashlight to see her....She was worth the trip!" he added as he cast a smile her way. She returned it. After marrying in 1937 they raised three children together while Fred worked construction before landing a job at Barton's Mines in 1944, where he forged a thirty-nine-year career, starting as a blacksmith and welder and eventually working his way up to shop foreman. After sixty-eight years of marriage, they still keep a comfortable home just past the post office in Bakers Mills.

Over the years, Fred has never lost his determination to protect and provide for Rita, especially when she faced the simultaneous health crises of colon cancer and severe hypertension several years ago. No matter how se-rious her problems might be, he will speak to her with a voice infinitely patient, soft, almost hypnotically nurturing in quality. Never belittling, overbearing or excessively controlling, his voice projects only concern, respect and compassion. In fact, when they come to my office in North Creek, they both address everyone around them in much the same way, without a trace of impatience or condescension. It is no wonder that they charm everyone that has the good fortune to meet them; they seem the Adirondack embodiment of Snow White and Prince Charming.

Even the most storybook marriage, however, must suffer challenges, and the Stewarts are no exception. On March 15, 2005, at the age of eighty-seven, Fred had been down on his hands and knees all day stripping wax off the kitchen floor. The job finally done, he was feeling tired and stepped outside at 5 PM to get a breath of fresh air. Rita recalls vividly what happened next. "I heard Fred cry out from the driveway and found that he had fallen on some black ice. His right leg was bent over sideways at the thigh and he was in awful pain. He told me to call 911 and not to move him. It broke my heart to see him lying there moaning in the cold because I couldn't help him myself." Within fifteen minutes the yard in front of their home was full of the cars of friends and neighbors who had heard the call on their scanners and had come to help while the rescue squad was dispatched from Johnsburg. As Fred was carefully lifted onto a stretcher and placed into the back of the ambulance, a sense of dread came over Rita. Waving goodbye to him as the squad headed to Glens Falls Hospital, "I was crying awful, and I cried all night. I was afraid I might not ever see him again..."

At the hospital, Fred's x-rays showed that he had suffered not only a mid-shaft fracture of the right femur or thigh bone, but a collapsed right

Fred and "Rita" Stewart on their Bakers Mills deck

lung as well. These injuries would have been potentially life-threatening even for a younger man. Receiving only spinal anesthesia to reduce risk, Fred required a steel plate, six screws and a metal cable to repair the fracture, while a chest tube was inserted between his ribs to re-expand his punctured lung. "Wasn't it awful being awake during the surgery?" I asked. His answer made me smile. "I was glad they let me stay awake," he said, "even though I could hear all the drilling and sawing. At least I could tell they knew what they were doing!" Despite his advanced age, Fred had one very powerful medicine working for him, and his daughter Linda delivered her to his bedside every day.

"Every day I saw him, he seemed a little better," Rita admitted. Within five days, Fred's chest tube was out, and only two days later he was already strong enough to be transferred to a rehab facility to continue his recovery. Although his injury would prevent him from being able to bear full weight on his right leg for six weeks, giving up was never an option. "Speaking for my brother Fred, my sister Janice and myself, dad is a very caring man with a positive attitude," Linda explained. "All the time my mother was worrying about him, his concern was for her, and he was frustrated when he wasn't there for her. The doctors said he did better than 98% of men his age, and we are convinced his devotion to her gave him the determination he needed to get better."

Today, when Fred and Rita come in to the North Creek Health Center for their visits, Fred walks a little slower and breathes a little harder than he did a year ago. But he still opens the door for his wife, and makes sure she has the most comfortable chair. To Fred, she remains the sweet young heartthrob he would walk through the dark to visit over seventy years ago, while he is still her Prince Charming. And to everyone at our health center, they remain the closest thing to royalty we have in these parts.

Winter scene near Bakers Mills

GORDON TUCKER – THE CONSTANT GARDENER

North Creek, July 2011

At first glance, Gordon Tucker seems to be living proof that a patient can be maddeningly noncompliant and yet enjoy a good quality of life on his own terms. By all accounts, Gordie's diabetes has been so out of control for so long that, at age seventy-one he shouldn't be living at all. It took me five years to convince him to quit smoking four packs a day, and after twenty five years he still refused to take insulin, causing his blood sugars to routinely run in the 300's. Whereas many patients as stubborn and hard-headed as he is are also apt to be obnoxious and disagreeable, Gordie is so likeable and disarming that he can almost make me believe that it is perfectly acceptable if I fail to get him to follow my advice. No matter how dire my warnings about the risk of stroke, blindness, kidney failure, heart attack, amputation, dementia and all the other horrors of advanced and uncontrolled diabetes, his response is always the same. With a calm and reassuring voice he'll say, as if to one of his grandchildren, "There now young fella, you needn't worry about me. I'll be okay." Even when offered free insulin supplies from the manufacturer, he would refuse. "I don't need that stuff," he would say.

Although Gordie has in fact suffered heart problems over the years which have left him with an implanted defibrillator and pacemaker due to diminished cardiac output, you would never know it by his appearance or behavior. He still has a full head of dark hair, the same lean physique, and a remarkable lack of the kidney, brain and other circulatory complications that I have been warning him about for the last quarter-century. He has not changed outwardly in all that time, and my

curiosity finally got the best of me a few years ago. During one particularly fruitless attempt to reason with him I threw my hands up in exasperation. "I really don't understand how you keep defying the odds after all these years," I said to him. "You have been an accident waiting to happen for decades- you must have some secret! What is it??" With his usual Zen-like serenity he replied, "Why don't you come over to my place sometime and I'll show you." Over the years he had talked briefly about his love of

The central vegetable garden from the Tucker's back porch

gardening since his retirement from a forty-year career at Barton's Mines, the world's largest provider of industrial garnet based in the tiny hamlet of North River, but I never considered it more than a minor diversion.

One sunny July day in 2009 I happened to be making home visits in his neighborhood and decided to take him up on his offer for a visit. I found his tidy home surrounded by a neatly manicured lawn and I could immediately tell that he spent a lot of time outdoors tending his property. His wife Pat greeted me at the door and, recognizing me, said with a knowing smile, "He's out back." As I made my way around the house, my eyes were met with a horticultural extravaganza that took my breath away. There were explosions of vines, vegetables and perennial flowers flourishing in every direction. Corn, zucchini, seven kinds of squash, white and Japanese cucumbers, two kinds of pumpkins, string and pole beans, three kinds of tomatoes, melons, and rhubarb were erupting from the soil in neat rows within the fenced vegetable garden, while beds of several kinds of bee balm, primrose, peonies, lupines and daisies surrounded the perimeter of the yard in a colorful garland ten feet deep. The whole plantation was overseen by two dachshunds, two chickens and a scarecrow.

"You must produce a ton of vegetables," I exclaimed with awe, surveying the spectacle. "Do you lose a lot to the deer and other animals?" "No," he replied, "the deer and I have an understanding. I leave a portion of the vegetables outside the fenced garden near the back of the house, so Pat and I can watch them eat what we offer from our back window, and they can see us. They never touch the rest- the chickens make sure of that." Clever.

"I guess this does keep you pretty busy," I admitted. He nodded. "You've got to stay active," he replied. "When I was young I used to be real active. I would hunt day and night, weekdays and weekends. Fred Stewart and I used to do it all together- ice fishing, trapping, trolling for pike, catching lake trout from a canoe, all that and more. Then I was in the Navy in the 1960's and saw Okinawa, the Philippines, Borneo, and was on the security detail at Pearl Harbor doing guard duty for ComSubPac. In 1963 I was late for my own wedding because I was on a destroyer escort, the *USS Hughes*, and we were chasing a Russian sub up and down the east coast right during the worst of the cold war. At Barton's Mines I did maintenance, welding, and mechanical

work. But this garden keeps me busy. It gives me something to look forward to. Each day you see a difference in the garden- sometimes you'll see a vine grown six inches in one day. And by the time I've finished weed-whacking, mowing the lawn, hoeing, raking, planting, picking and pruning I've gotten a lot of exercise. Pat too; she might pick a bushel of vegetables in a day and then go around town giving them to folks that can use them." As if on cue, Pat handed me a shopping bag full of zucchini and yellow squash, some as big as bowling pins!

Taking care of Gordon Tucker's health has been a humbling lesson, but in a good way. The experience reminds me that a healthy lifestyle which involves a passion requiring physical exercise, inhaling large amounts of fresh Adirondack air and communing with the natural world while providing healthy home-grown food is a more powerful elixir than any prescription drug. In essence, Gordie lives a lifestyle which has almost disappeared in the age of fast food, supermarkets and pizza parlors offering home delivery. He also reminded me that physicians who want to better understand their patients must sometimes look beyond the confines of the office to fully appreciate what motivates them.

Not long after my visit to Gordie's garden, a funny thing happened… he agreed to start insulin!

Tilling the soil

Gordon and Patricia Tucker in their garden

48

BARBARA ROSS - CAREGIVER

Baker's Mills, February 2007

New York State Route 8 is a country road that passes through some of the least-populated areas in the Adirondack Park. Beginning at the western shore of Lake George at Hague, it winds its way through such villages as Brant Lake, Chestertown, Wevertown, Johnsburg, Sodom, Speculator, Piseco Lake and Hoffmeister before exiting the park at Poland. Just northwest of Sodom lies a tiny settlement called Bakers Mills that is perched on Route 8 like a chickadee on a telephone wire. If it wasn't for the rustic schoolhouse and Wesleyan church that command the view along route 8 as you negotiate the curve past Edwards Hill Road, or the lure of J & J's Fox Lair Tavern, you might not even realize you had been in a town at all. In its heyday it sported farms and sawmills, and for a time boasted the elegant Foxlair estate built by perfume and cosmetics tycoon Richard Alexander Hudnut during the gilded age of a century ago. Today's inhabitants include several clans that can trace their Bakers Mills roots back many generations, including the Ross, Cleveland, Hitchcock and Allen families.

In the 1920's, Arnold Ross married Gretchen Cleveland and they started a family while running a typical subsistence farm that met most of their needs for many years. Gretchen began taking on foster children even as she was having children of her own, and later they opened the Sunrise Grocery along Route 8, where the folks in Bakers Mills and Sodom could buy the staples of everyday life. Gretchen's children Harold, Harriet, Harry, Howard, Joseph, Barbara and James helped out at the store and the family farm but as the years passed, they grew up and began to carve out lives of their own in town. Harriet married George Allen and found work at the nursing home on the other side of Gore Mountain in North Creek. Harold married Isabelle Hitchcock and made a living in a variety of ways that allowed him to stay in town (see his vignette in *All in a Day's Work*). Jim married Marilyn Osgood and made a career in the garnet mines of North River. Meanwhile Barbara, the youngest daughter, inherited the role of helping her mother care for the foster children. In those times, a young girl in a large rural Adirondack family did what she was told. At first, she didn't mind.

The Wesleyan Church site along Route 8

49

"I loved the children," Barbara recalls, "but it was never my choice what I did." Well into adulthood, her mother's influence became stronger rather than weaker, as did the effect on Barb's individuality. "Mom always wanted me to do just what she wanted… I couldn't develop myself because I was living mom's life." Well into her seventies now, Barb was telling me this from her home on Route 8, just across the street from Harold's potato farm and down the road from the Wesleyan Church where as a young girl she could escape family responsibilities for a couple hours every week. I had come by to see how she was doing after she had signed out of an assisted-living facility in Warrensburg to return to the family homestead where she had increasing difficulty functioning independently…. the home where she lived with her mother after everyone else had left… and where she had become her mother's sole caregiver for six years until Gretchen passed away in 2003.

I had first met Barbara Ross over twenty years earlier when she would bring Gretchen in for her visits, and I had noticed how attentive she was to her mother's needs. When I recalled this to her, Barb agreed. "I took care of mom," she said with pride. "I done her every wish. It got to the

Barb's living room

point where I could tell what she wanted even when she would just look at me…she didn't have to say anything. That's why she wanted to be with me when she was older because I knew what was wrong with her before she even said it." Knowing Barb had never married or had children of her own, I asked if she had ever lived away from her mother. "I tried living in Syracuse and Schenectady for a while," she said, "but I came home because I didn't want to be away from my mother. I felt like I needed to be with her no matter what she said or done to me. But she knew that, and she played on it." Like many such mother-daughter relationships, this one was characterized by a degree of mutual dependence that became unhealthy for both parties.

As the years passed, Barb's relationship with Gretchen became strained. "She knew all of my weak spots and knew what buttons to push." After her step-father Ralph Millington died, Barb was the only one who would (and could) take care of her mother. Gretchen became more anxious and housebound with age, and for those last six years she became almost totally dependant on Barb. Recalling those times as I sat across the table from her in her living room, her brow furrowed. "Sometimes with mom I couldn't even go into the kitchen and leave her here. I don't know why- whether it was because she was lonesome or scared or what." Instead of sleeping in the separate bedrooms upstairs Barb moved their two beds into the living room where she could sleep within a few feet of Gretchen.

By the time Gretchen died, the psychological toll on Barb was apparent. She had no skills to get a job, and the vacuum left by her mother's passing left her feeling guilty, depressed and restless. Looking at me she admitted "I kept expecting to see her sitting at this table- right where you are now." Barb's own health began to suffer, ultimately resulting in coronary artery disease in 2005. She needed the help of Harriet and Jim to get by and became increasingly isolated, especially when she became unable to drive her car. Finally, in the fall of 2006, I suggested she consider relocating to an assisted living home in Warrensburg. "You'll have all the support you need there, and you won't be alone," I reasoned. "There are other folks from Bakers Mills there, and you could reconnect with them. You might even make new friends and provide comfort and support to them." After giving it some thought, she agreed.

"For a while I felt good there," she was telling me later. "Everyone was good to me, and it was a nice change from being by myself. I saw Rita Stewart (whose husband Fred had passed by then) and some other folks I knew, and I tried to help them if they needed anything." Her siblings and I were hopeful she would find peace of mind there and settle in to a comfortable and safe environment, but it was not to be. Within a few months she was back in her Bakers Mills home. I had scheduled a home visit for a few weeks after her return, certain that I would find her once again beset by the haunting influence of her mother. Crossing the threshold with some apprehension, I found Barb sitting at the table, reading her family bible and looking out at Edwards Hill in the distance. Taking my seat across from her, I was expecting an outpouring of regret and self-reproach for having moved back home. Instead, I was greeted with a smile of contentment I had not seen on her face in many years. Barb's inner demons seemed to have vanished- she was happy! After hearing a recounting of her experience at the adult home, I asked her what had changed to make her want to come back.

"I got so I realized I couldn't help the other folks the way I wanted, and it just didn't feel right." Barb also received some timely counseling from Suzanne Tomb, our psychiatric social worker who was able to establish a good rapport with Barb even before her move to Warrensburg. This helped her to see things in a new light. "Maybe you finally learned that what you were searching for was right inside you all along," I suggested.

She nodded. "There isn't a lot of trouble here now. I'm the same as I was before leaving, but that's all gone. Before, it was like it was mom's house and I was just living in it. Now it's my place. And I can do what I want here."

Who says you can never go home again?

Barb's home on Route 8

51

THE MOFFITT FAMILY

Wevertown- July 2007

The Moffitt family lives on a dirt road in Wevertown, where they eke out an existence against daunting odds. Every member of the Vincent and Janet Moffitt family has a chronic health problem of some kind, yet they carry on despite having their home burned to the ground twice by electrical fires. Daughter Denise had open-heart surgery for congenital heart disease at age thirteen, and seven pacemakers implanted over the ensuing twenty-nine years. Her twenty-year-old son Clifford has a seizure disorder and severe learning disabilities. Janet, standing in the doorway, has osteoarthritis, but has become the head of the household since husband Vincent, a former laborer and lumberjack, developed Alzheimer's disease over five years ago.

"It hurts to pay the $25 copays every month for each of our medicines," says Janet, "but without Medicaid, we wouldn't have nothin'! I promised Vince I wouldn't put him in a nursing home, and I'm going to try to keep that promise as long as I can." In the Adirondacks, family ties are often strongest where there is the least money. They survive by pooling their limited resources, and that holds them together. They have almost no disposable income, and yet Janet has managed to gather and collect innumerable lawn ornaments and knick-knacks which has transformed their property into an amazing work of folk art.

Vincent's mother, the late Beatrice Moffitt, died only a few months before this family portrait was taken. She had been the matriarch and role model for the extended family, and set quite an example in terms of stubborn independence. At age seventy-six Bea suffered a stroke caused by hyperthyroidism and heart problems that left her with a right sided paralysis and almost total loss of speech. Like so many headstrong, old-school, Adirondack matriarchs with dedicated children, Bea continued to dictate the terms of her care which her caregiver daughter Charlotte and I (as her physician) obeyed. Refusing the cost and inconvenience of blood thinners used to prevent another stroke, Bea took only aspirin, digoxin and anti-

(Left to right) Denise, Clifford, Vincent and Janet Moffitt

53

thyroid medication for the rest of her life while Charlotte single-handedly took care of her in the tiny home they shared. Bea finally died at the ripe old age of ninety-four, eighteen years after her stroke, without spending another night in a hospital or nursing home.

This is why I find these worthy residents of the Adirondack Park so remarkable; they resemble the average rural American family from several generations ago. What they lack in financial resources, they more than make up for in dignity, self-respect, and remarkable survival skills.

Beatrice and Charlotte Moffitt home

Beatrice Moffitt and her daughter Charlotte Springer

DAWN VANSELOW – ADIRONDACK REBEL

Pottersville, 2006

One thing I can always count on when I begin my day's work at the North Creek and Indian Lake Health Centers is that, before the day ends, at least one Adirondack Character will have come through the door. To be considered a blue-blooded Adirondack Character it helps to have been born in the North Country, and you get extra credit if you can trace your Adirondack family roots back a couple centuries to old white dudes wearing buckskin and toting muzzle-loaders. To really qualify as an Adirondack Character though, one must also exhibit a certain degree of stubborn independence and harbor strong opinions. On all counts, Dawn Vanselow is a true Adirondack Character, but with a twist. Most Adirondack Characters tend to lean to the right politically and philosophically, perhaps because of their passionate belief in property rights, gun rights, and patriotism. Dawn represents a rarer subspecies of Adirondack Character- she leans to the left. I learned how far left one day when she came to see me in May 2006.

Like most of my long-standing patients, Dawn has learned to bring a book to read while waiting to see me. I entered the exam room to find her engrossed in Bill Maher's *New Rules*, a liberal manifesto if ever there was one. Wearing a colorful floral print dress and sporting her trademark pigtails, she seemed ready for a 1960's sit-in protest at some college campus. When I pointed this out to her, she dryly replied, "been there, done that." At the end of our visit she invited me to her Pottersville home to continue our conversation. How could I refuse?

Over tea a few weeks later, I learned that she was a Morehouse by birth, a name associated with the earliest Adirondack settlers. The daughter of a

Methodist minister, she was born in Gloversville but moved frequently during her childhood, living in Rochester, Olean, Buffalo, Syracuse, and Elmira. But, as she told me, "every summer we came back to the cabin near the Hudson River in Riparius that my father had built before I was born, and to me it has always been home. I have always had an appreciation for the Adirondacks." As a child she gained that appreciation for the Adirondacks one summer after contracting rheumatic fever. "I had to stay in bed for an entire month," she recalled. "When the doctor finally let me out of bed, I couldn't wait to get outdoors. I was very weak at first, so I imagined climbing Carpenter Mountain behind our house to regain my strength. Eventually I was climbing it twelve times a day! The woods and mountains here have great healing powers, at least for me." They would heal her more than once in her life.

I asked her if she was raised in a liberal-minded environment; her bemused look told otherwise. "I grew up in a conservative Republican family," she explained. "But as I got out into the world and began paying attention to things, it changed my entire outlook on life- and I started thinking for myself." With my next question "what was your favorite decade?" I guessed correctly. "The Sixties," she said without hesitation. "I was married and living in Greensboro, North Carolina, where my husband was a chemistry professor at UNC. I was raising a houseful of teenagers and it was a hectic but exciting time. The family car was a VW minibus. I saw Joan Baez and Peter, Paul and Mary at the Greensboro Coliseum in their heyday, and carried candles with my three oldest kids in a peace rally during the Viet Nam War in 1965. We had a run-in with the Black Panthers at the end of the march- that was fun! Now it seems like a million years ago."

Dawn Vanselow keeping the liberal faith

By 1986, after a painful divorce, she found herself back full time in the Riparius cabin that her father built. She has lived in the Adirondacks ever since, and five of her seven children have followed her back. I couldn't resist asking her to compare the direction our country was going in 2006 to 1966. "Where do I begin?" she moaned. "The (George W. Bush) administration's total takeover of all our rights, privileges, defying the constitution, making their own laws, and nobody stops them. Congress just sits there like a bump on a log and gets walked all over- it's getting harder and harder to accept. I think it's dangerous. I'm scared for my children and grandchildren." She takes some comfort from living in the Adirondacks, even if her political views are considered sacrilegious by many of her neighbors. "We know how each of us feels and we don't discuss it. I can't change my stripes. I was born a rebel, and I grew up a rebel. I guess I'm still a rebel!"

Hudson River in Riparius, near Dawn's cabin

JOHN ARCHAMBEAU RETIRED SAWYER

North Creek- May 2007

John Archambeau has a great face. Part Native American, part French Canadian, with some Persian and Irish blood blended in for good measure, his features seem to reflect the iconic Adirondack Male. There is gentleness in his eyes, serenity in his brow, strength in his jaw, and vigor in his thick mane of unruly hair. In reality, he's a nice guy and a family man who likes the simple pleasures of life. He enjoyed his work as a sawyer in various Adirondack sawmills, despite the innumerable splinters, cuts, calluses, back and shoulder strains that cut short his career. Now he plays the role of grandfather and patriarch, all before the age of fifty.

John looks like a man who loves living in the Adirondack forest, and he truly does. In fact, like many Adirondack men, he has a special appreciation for the trees that surround his modest home outside of North Creek that he shares with his significant other Nancy Holland, daughter Johnie, and grandson Matthew. Knowing the family survives on his disability benefits, I asked him if he ever considered moving out of the woods into a more urban environment where he might find some employment which would not require heavy labor.

"I'd rather have my trees," he answered. "There's no money to be made up here per se, but if I can't have a lot of money then I'd rather live up here. I love the woods. I can go all day in the woods and not be tired,

but I feel tired when I'm in a city like Glens Falls. I saw on TV that one tree makes enough oxygen for four people. So when you go to the city and there's not one tree around, where are the people getting their oxygen from? Pollution is bad and there's not enough oxygen in the cities." But didn't he get lonely or bored out in his woods? Doesn't he have any regrets? "I've worked in sawmills all my life, and even though I can't do it anymore, I wouldn't change anything. I like people but I don't like to be close to them all the time."

Spoken like a true Adirondacker!

John with grandson Matthew

CHARLIE KAYS – FIRE WARDEN & PROPERTY CARETAKER

Olmstedville, September 2003

Charlie Kays has the biggest hands I have ever seen. Although I myself wear size eight gloves and can spread my fingers about ten inches, my hand disappears into Charlie's when we greet each other. I have seen baseball mitts smaller than his hands. "When I was twelve, my school-teacher would always ask me to get the dictionary if we needed to learn how to spell a word" he recalls. "I was the only kid in the Olmstedville School who could pick up and hold the Webster's Dictionary in one hand." Actually, Charlie is a big man all the way around. Even at the mature age of eighty-eight, he tops six-feet-six in height. "That's probably why the state hired me to man the fire tower on Vanderwhacker Mountain back in 1963. I could see just a little farther than anyone else up there." For two summers he lived in a cabin half-way up the mountain, and every morning he would climb to the top of the tower to scan the horizon for signs of a fire. "I would spend a whole day watching birds come into my tower where I would feed them berries and seeds, and once in a while some hikers would come up, so I didn't feel alone much." He admits that the solitude and the mountain's remoteness ultimately led him to one of the many career changes that he made. "I wanted something that would keep me a little busier," he reflects.

As big as he is, Charlie seems even bigger when I visit him in his humble home along Donnelly road in Olmstedville. It is a classic Adirondack bungalow; small, simple, one story, with a low ceiling, and altogether adequate for his needs. On the pine-paneled wall behind him, over a dozen partridge tails attest to his hunting skills. When Charlie stands up, the room seems to shrink. It's easy to visualize him handling a team of horses snaking logs through the forests outside Newcomb for Finch, Pruyn as he did during the 1940's, or taking care of the North Woods Club in Minerva as he did after the fire tower gig was up, or operating graders and bulldozers for the town of Minerva as he did for over twenty years. He still looks as though he could operate heavy equipment today.

I often see Charlie crossing the parking lot with his long, measured strides from my office window at North Creek when he comes to visit his wife Margaret and other Olmstedville residents at the Adirondack Tri-County Nursing Home next door. It always brings a smile to my face, especially when I am having a hectic day seeing patients, being interrupted with phone calls, and shuffling endless mountains of paperwork. I think of Charlie up in the Vanderwhacker Mountain tower quietly playing with the blue jays and finches in one of the most remote areas of the Adirondack wilderness, and how he gave it up when he couldn't stand the quiet isolation anymore. I would sooooo much like to know what that feels like!

Ranger's cabin and Vanderwhacker Mountain Wilderness from Goodnow Mountain fire tower.

JACQUELINE GALUSHA – RESORT OWNER

Indian Lake, August 2011

Every now and then as I see a patient at the Indian Lake Health Center, I can almost feel what it must have been like for my great-grandfather when he had to serve on picket duty during the Civil War. I am on the front line, alone in the wilderness and far from others in my profession, defending a population who depend on me to shield them from attack. When I am successful, I can help to save lives, and when I am unsuccessful, I may fail to prevent the suffering or even death of someone I am pledged to protect. On an average day at my rural health center, it's hard to forget that the continued health of every person who walks through the door is my responsibility. The majority of my time is devoted to routine health care maintenance, where I screen and evaluate patients for common diseases and conditions, while providing counseling and treatment to prevent them. Every day I have the opportunity to prevent or detect diseases such as cancer and atherosclerosis that kill millions of Americans each year. Over the years I have probably helped to save many lives by simply ordering mammograms, prescribing medications that control elevated cholesterol and blood pressure, providing immunizations, examining prostates, referring patients for colonoscopies and convincing people to quit smoking. Likewise, I have lost patients from cancer, infectious diseases, heart attacks and many other causes. Even the most innocent encounter can lead to unexpected results. Sometimes it can make a rural health care provider feel very vulnerable.

Consider the case of Jacqueline Galusha, a resourceful woman a few years younger than myself who operates the family resort on Lewey Lake, halfway between the tiny Hamilton County hamlets of Indian Lake and

Jackie Galusha, taking care of business at Lewey Lake

Speculator. Composed of eighteen housekeeping cottages on one hundred acres commanding a breathtaking view of the Snowy Mountain range directly across the lake, maintaining Galusha's Cabins is a full-time maintenance job for Jackie, even with the help she gets from friends and family. Her responsibilities include booking reservations, paying bills, grounds keeping, housekeeping, maintenance, and repairs that range from fixing leaky pipes to rebuilding roofs. Being the True Adirondacker that she is, however, Jackie also worked for thirty-one years at the Hamilton County Department of Social Services which not only provided extra income but health care benefits as well. What her lifestyle lacks, however, is free time, especially during the summer tourism season. As a result, Jackie is not exactly a frequent visitor to my office, and when she does come to see me she is usually suffering a flare-up of her asthmatic bronchitis or recurrent sinusitis.

So it was that she came to see me on June 21, 2009 coughing and wheezing, with a headache and sore throat, looking for a quick fix so she could get back to fixing a leaky faucet. Having treated her for this several times in the past, it took only a few minutes to listen to her lungs, examine her ears, sinuses and throat, then devise a treatment plan that would get her back to work. Quickly scanning her vital signs in the chart as I prescribed the necessary medications, I noticed that she had lost twenty five pounds since her last visit. "I see you've lost some weight," I said casually. "Do you have so much to do that you're too busy to eat?" "Pretty much," she wheezed. Then she added in a puzzled tone, almost as an afterthought, "So if I'm losing weight, how come my stomach is getting bigger?" Processing her answer in my mind, I suddenly felt a twinge of fear, much as a sentry on picket duty might upon hearing a twig snap in the dark.

Studying my face as I examined her, she asked "What's wrong?" My expression betrayed my concern, as I was feeling a large mass in her lower abdomen. "I guess you got more than you bargained for today," I said uneasily, and explained that I was feeling something that was not supposed to be there which would have to be diagnosed and treated as soon as possible. A visit that had started as a routine chest cold had become much more complicated. Later she would explain her reluctance to address her concern about the weight loss: "I'm a private person and I didn't want to think there was something really wrong, so I didn't mention it to the nurse when she brought me into the exam room. I just knew I wasn't right."

When a CT scan confirmed a large ovarian mass, I notified Jackie of the results and recommended referral to Dr. Daniel Kredentser two hours' driving away in Albany who specialized in gynecologic cancer surgery. Over the phone lines we both felt the unspoken anguish of not knowing in advance whether the mass was benign, malignant, or a mixture of both. "If anyone can fix this," I tried to assure her, "he can."

Years later, Jackie recounted what went through her mind after seeing the surgeon. "Emotionally it's tough," she said. "I knew there was something wrong but I wasn't sure what. It was scary- extremely scary. They told me it was a tumor so I knew it could be cancer- I was afraid of the anesthesia because I don't do well with that. And I was down in St. Peters Hospital which was very far from home. And I have all this work I had to do, and now I'm going to be laid up, and they would have to make a very large incision, and you lose a lot of muscle tone, and it takes a long time to get back in shape to do the things I have to do." Fortunately, her surgery was successful, revealing a mostly benign tumor as big as a football in which a small core of malignant cells was just beginning to develop. She would make a full recovery with an excellent prognosis.

Years later, Jackie is still running her resort on Lewey Lake, and I notice she is more willing to come in once a year for a visit. She admits that facing a potentially life-threatening illness made her less apt to take her health for granted. As she put it, "It made me realize that you have to pay attention to what your body is telling you." For me, it was a reminder that, after being on picket duty for over thirty years, I must remain vigilant. People I know personally put their lives in my hands, and I must seize every opportunity to protect them, whether it be getting another smoker to quit, provide a pneumonia vaccine to a septuagenarian, or ask the right questions when I see a change in someone's appearance.

At the end of a long day, when my staff have all gone home, I still have to type the last electronic progress note and clear out the flood of lab test results from my computer's in-box. I then turn out the lights, climb into my Subaru Outback, and begin the fifty-three-mile commute from Indian Lake to my Glens Falls home. Along the way, I listen to some favorite music to unwind- anything from U2 or Jethro Tull when I'm upbeat and wired, to Strauss Waltzes or Loreena McKinnitt's Celtic masterpieces when I'm more pensive or tired. By the time I reach home, the music will have purged the day's work from my mind, and I morph from rural physician back to private citizen. I am off picket duty- until tomorrow morning.

Snowy Mountain from Galusha's Cabins resort

CORA WALDRON – MATRIARCH

North Creek, May 2005

Some people are born fighters. If asked to conjure an image of the quintessential fighter, we might picture Muhammad Ali standing over a defeated opponent in the boxing ring; General Ulysses Grant astride his war horse, or Dr. Jonas Salk in his lab striving to find a way to eradicate polio. In my own little world, the battlefield is often Glens Falls Hospital. In that arena, one of the greatest fighters I have ever known is Cora Waldron of North Creek. This tenacious woman is eighty-four years old, weighs only eighty-nine pounds and is crippled by rheumatoid arthritis and a chronic lung disease called bronchiectasis, but to me she is right up there with the great Ali.

For older folks with chronic lung disease, winter is a season to be endured and hopefully survived. The waves of influenza, pneumonia and bronchitis that pass through our tiny Adirondack communities during those cold, dark months take their toll every year. People like Cora try to stay home and out of harm's way, hoping the unseen but deadly enemy will pass them by. But one night in January of 2005, Cora knew she had a fight on her hands. "First, I started feeling weaker and lost my appetite," she told me. "I was coughing more and knew I was getting sick, but I didn't want to go back to the hospital again." A severe skin infection had landed her in Glens Falls Hospital for a month the previous year, and despite the good care she received there, the memories were not pleasant. Her daughter Evelyn, who lives with her, became worried and suggested she be seen in the hospital's emergency room. Cora, who is more inclined to give orders than take them, resisted for several days, until she began experiencing symptoms of pleurisy. When she became too weak to argue,

Evelyn called the North Creek rescue squad. By the time Cora arrived at the emergency care center at Glens Falls Hospital, she was in severe respiratory distress, an extensive pneumonia had filled most of her right lung, and she was at great risk of suffering acute respiratory failure. The emergency room physician, Jeff Flynn, could see that the combination of frailty and advanced age put Cora in imminent danger of dying. Knowing that many patients at her stage of life might have advanced directives forbidding life support measures, he explained the danger she was in and advised that endotracheal intubation and mechanical ventilation would be the only way to save her life. He asked her if she would allow him to put a breathing tube in her windpipe. Fighting for every breath from behind her oxygen mask, she looked at him with a piercing stare as if to say "what kind of a dumb question is that?" Instead, the last words she would speak for thirty-seven days were "do it."

Anyone familiar with full life support knows what happened next. After being given intravenous sedation, Cora had a plastic tube passed down her throat into her trachea, a balloon around its lower end was inflated to make a seal, and the upper end was connected with a hose to a programmable ventilator that would push oxygen into her lungs, while the airways could be suctioned clear of obstructing secretions. Since swallowing becomes impossible around the ET, or endotracheal tube, a nasogastric tube was passed through the nose, into the back of the throat, and down the esophagus to the stomach so that medications and tube feedings could be given around the clock. Two intravenous catheters were inserted in her arms to administer fluids and powerful antibiotics, while another catheter was inserted into the bladder to measure urinary output. Sedation was mercifully continued to allow her to relax and conserve energy, while her

Cora Waldron in her favorite chair

arms were restrained to prevent her from accidentally pulling out the life-sustaining tubes in her nose and mouth should she awaken. Cora was then admitted to the intensive care unit where three cardiac monitor electrodes were placed on her chest wall and attached to wires, allowing continuous monitoring of her heart rhythm. An oxygen sensor was clipped to her finger and a blood pressure cuff was wrapped around her arm. Many blood samples were drawn from her veins and arteries to further assess her condition. And so the battle was on. Her chances of leaving the hospital alive were poor, but she had made it clear she was willing to put up a fight.

Her tests would reveal the presence of a bacterium called *Pseudomonas aeruginosa* in her lungs and bloodstream, one of the hardest germs to kill with even the most powerful antibiotics. She was started on intravenous Primaxim and Azactam, sometimes referred to as 'gorillacillin' for their potency. On the fourth day of her hospitalization, a CT scan revealed the need for a surgeon to insert a chest tube between her ribs to drain a large abscess that had formed around her lung, and it was connected to a suction device that would drain the infection over several days. At the same time she underwent the first of four bronchoscopies, where a fiberoptic scope was passed down her ET tube to examine the airways and suction out infected secretions far down in her lungs. On day seven, another drug called streptokinase was injected through her chest tube directly into the abscess cavity to dissolve and remove inflammatory debris. On day eight, another antibiotic, Zyvox, was added to treat another deadly bacterium called methcillin-resistant *Staphylococcus aureus*, or MRSA. She was then weaned off sedation and awoke to find six catheters in her body and unable to speak, swallow or breathe on her own. Rather than panic however, she immediately understood the situation and her first request, made with gestures, was to have her arms untied. At first my colleagues hesitated, knowing how commonly patients would pull out their tubes in a moment of confusion. But when she gave Dr. Paul Bachman the same piercing stare she had aimed at the emergency room physician, he relented. For the rest of her ordeal she would require no further restraints or sedation and never pulled out any of her catheters.

On day nine, she became even sicker when she developed a serious and painful new infection, this time in her intestine. A fourth antibiotic metronidazole was started, this time down her NG tube. When further attempts to wean her off the respirator were unsuccessful, she underwent a second bronchoscopy on day twelve, and more infected secretions were removed. By the time it was my turn in the rotation to care for the hospitalized patients in our large practice, her ET and NG tubes had been in so long that they would have to be removed to prevent erosive ulcerations of her trachea and esophagus. I explained all of this to her and provided a summary of her hospital stay over the past two weeks, ending with a frank assessment of her prognosis, which remained poor. "We don't have to keep doing this if you don't want us to Cora," I assured her. "If you think we have been too aggressive with your treatment and you would rather we pulled out all these tubes and just kept you comfortable for whatever time you have left, we will. If you want to keep fighting though, you'll have to allow us to put an opening in your throat for a tracheostomy, and another in your abdominal wall, so we can put the breathing and feeding tubes directly into your windpipe and stomach. Are you ready to let go, or do you want to keep on fighting?" Expecting that she might opt for simple comfort measures, instead I was the next victim of The Stare. The look in her penetrating blue eyes seemed to go right through me, making me feel almost ashamed for asking the question. I looked over at Evelyn, who laughed and said, "I know that look. You better do what she wants!" Like a boxer lifting himself off the canvas after a knockdown, Cora still had some fight left in her.

After a tracheostomy on day sixteen and placement of a gastrostomy tube on day eighteen, Cora required three more antibiotic changes to keep her infections under control, and a third bronchoscopy was needed on day twenty-seven after she again could not be weaned off the ventilator. Witnessing her ordeal, her extended family members suffered along with Cora, but supported her faithfully. "You don't argue with my mother," Evelyn said. "She always knew what was best for us when we were kids, and I figure she knows what's best for her too."

On the thirtieth day, her antibiotics were changed yet again, this time to meropenem and ciprofloxacin, drugs that are strong enough to kill anthrax. Gradually, she began showing signs of improvement. A fourth bronchoscopy on day thirty-four revealed that her lungs were finally clearing. Because she was so cooperative, she was able to tolerate being lifted out of bed into a chair while still on the respirator, and she began bearing weight for the first

Cora's home's distinctive red roof

time in weeks. On day thirty-seven she was at last able to breathe on her own through the tracheostomy, and her respirator was turned off with much fanfare. On the forty-first day, she was able to eat real food and her tracheostomy tube was removed. After enduring the innumerable needle sticks, catheters, airway suctioning, x-rays, bed baths, physical therapy sessions, sleep interruptions and bronchoscopies, the first words she rasped through her weakened vocal chords were "I want to go home!"

Having survived an ordeal that would have killed almost anyone else, Cora had only begun her long recovery. She had become so weak and deconditioned that she would need to spend twenty-three more days in the hospital before she was medically stable enough to be transferred to the Adirondack Tri-County Rehabilitation and Nursing Care Facility which was only a mile from her home. Its proximity and familiarity only made Cora's determination to recover stronger. She forced herself to eat enough food to restore her strength and muscle mass, even when her stomach felt that it might burst. Fighting the wish to stay in bed, she endured walking, weight lifting and breathing exercises with the coaxing and support of the many nurses, therapists and aides that formed her fan club. They all remember getting The Stare when they would make her work a little too hard, but they kept working at it anyway.

Finally, after sixty-five days in Glens Falls Hospital and 110 more in the Adirondack Tri-County Health Care Facility, Cora had achieved what had seemed impossible in January 2005. She was ready to go home. She remembers the date July 11, 2005 well. "After all those months, I finally felt like it had all been worthwhile," she told me. Having fought so hard to return home, she was determined not to leave it again. Rather than force her to come to my office for visits, I began visiting her in her Main Street home, across from the firehouse. She had already been home for a week or two when I made my first visit, and the regular reports from the visiting Warren County public health nurses were upbeat. She was eating well and breathing comfortably on concentrated oxygen. A hospital bed had been installed in a room next to the kitchen so she could navigate independently with her walker, since Evelyn had returned to work and Cora was alone much of the day. This suited Cora just fine.

On my first visit, I decided to document Cora's heroic battle, and she gave me permission to bring my cameras on my next visit. A month later she was still doing well and as I deployed my Nikon and Bronica, I asked her if she could walk into the living room and sit in her favorite chair by the window, where the light was best. With great effort she walked the length of her house and plopped down in the welcoming softness of her recliner, where her collection of exquisite antique dolls observed us from above. Obviously pleased with herself, she announced, "This is the first time I have sat in this chair since I came home!"

A year after Cora left Glens Falls Hospital, she remains at home as of this writing. Having raised her children and grandchildren there, she doesn't want to be anywhere else. To Cora, home represents a sanctuary- where she can be alone, in her own space, surrounded by her own things, able to eat in her own kitchen, sleep in her own bedroom, enveloped in peace and quiet. Most of us would take this for granted, but not Cora. She had to work hard for it. On a recent visit, I asked Cora if her long battle had been worth it. "Of course!" she replied. "I knew I would make it home. I thought about it every day that I was in the hospital. That's what kept me going."

As her physician, and wanting to update Cora's advance directives about resuscitation, I had to ask her one more question as I was writing my notes in her chart. "What if you got sick again- would you be willing to go back to the hospital? Would you accept a respirator again?" Hearing no response, I looked up to see if she had heard me. She had. She was giving me The Stare.

JOSEPH BATEMAN – HANDYMAN AND CAREGIVER

Johnsburg, December 2011

As the American birth rate declines and our ability to control common diseases like diabetes and heart failure improves, our population has been aging. As a result, there are more frail, elderly people in need of support, with relatively fewer young people willing and able to care for them. Nowhere in the United States (except the gulf coast of Florida) is this truer than in the Adirondack Park. The average age of an Adirondacker is now over forty-four, and increasing every year as young people move to more urbanized environments where it is easier to make a living and enjoy modern American conveniences. Older native Adirondackers are at risk for losing their support systems when they become too debilitated to drive a car, maintain their homes or handle their own finances. Over their long lives they sink their spiritual roots so deeply into the bedrock of their beloved woods and mountains that trying to uproot and transplant them into nursing homes or the houses of their children can be as difficult as pulling a mule out of a bog. Most would prefer to stay in the homes they grew up and raised their family in until their last breath.

A century ago, many Adirondackers lived on family farms where there were three or more generations under the same roof sharing the same resources and duties. The frail elders would stay home and be cared for by their descendants. When their health failed they would die at home, surrounded by their loved ones, usually without a doctor or nurse in sight. As families have become smaller and domestic farms have been replaced by households where every adult may have at least two jobs to survive, this pattern has been largely replaced by one that involves the elders spending their last days (or years)

Garnet Lake valley and road from Crane Mountain summit

in nursing homes, where the doctors, nurses, aides and therapists become 'family'. Although this is a necessary environment for many of our disabled seniors, there are still some parent-child relationships which remain so strong that the adult children are willing to dedicate their lives to keeping their parents in their own home, even when it means giving up their own freedom for months or years. You have already read about Barbara Ross, but now I want you to meet Joseph Bateman.

The two-hundred-year-old Bateman farmhouse is located in rural Johnsburg under the shadow of Crane Mountain, whose massive granite slopes shield the adjacent valley along Garnet Lake Road from modern life. When Clarence "Bud" Bateman married Jean Richards in 1947, the couple became the youngest of three generations living in the family home. At the time, the house was part of his grandfather's Garnet Dairy Farm, named for the nearby garnet mines. Over the years, Bud also worked for the town of Johnsburg, ran an excavation business, and was the last fire warden on Gore Mountain. He and Jean added nine children to the family, many of whom still live nearby. Sixty-five years later, the farmhouse, barns and fields survive, but Bud and Jean are well into their eighties and have become dependent on their children for support. While most of their children have families of their own and devote what time they can spare to help their parents, the youngest son Joseph has been the only one who could move in to provide 24/7 care. A natural jack-of-all trades, Joe has worked various jobs over the years as a logger, excavator, gravel hauler, plumber, stonemason and sawyer, usually self-employed. But as a young man Joe had problems of his own.

When I first met Joe over ten years ago, he wasn't even taking care of himself. The casual observer might have dismissed him as just another unmarried mountain man who was in the habit of spending what little money he had on alcohol; and in his younger days this was an accurate assessment. He had come to me for help, and seemed very sincere about changing his life. "I wanted to quit drinking because it was a choice of whether I wanted to live or die," he says now in his usual matter-of-fact manner. "I just didn't want it anymore." He needed a safe haven to clean up his life, and his folks needed someone with dedication, determination

Joseph Bateman outside the family homestead

and a gift for improvisation. Fortunately for Bud and Jean, Joseph has these traits in abundance.

Once committed, Joe quickly began learning the skills of a caregiver. His father is a gentle soul whose health has been especially devastated by diabetes, heart issues and lung disease. When Bud's emphysema advanced enough to require a home nebulizer, Joe learned how to operate it for his dad. When Bud's diabetes worsened, Joe learned how to monitor his dad's blood sugar. And when Bud developed a foot infection that ultimately required hospitalization and amputation of his gangrenous right fifth toe, Joe stayed at the hospital day and night to ensure Bud was properly attended to while watching how the nurses dressed the wound. Then Joe took his dad home where he changed the dressing, prepared nutritious meals, made frequent runs to the drug store, administered the many medications, gave sponge baths, helped Bud to the commode, offered many words of encouragement, and all the other endless tasks that caregiving demands. When Bud stopped eating and began bleeding from the stomach, Joe took his dad down to Glens Falls Hospital for outpatient transfusions, then shot a deer to provide him with the only high-protein food his dad would eat- fresh venison steaks cooked on the grill. Over time, the bleeding stopped and the foot healed, all without hospital readmission or nursing home placement.

As hard as it has been for Joe to learn the technical skills, mastering the psychological aspects of caregiving has been even harder. To his credit, he has developed a philosophical approach that makes it easier to cope. "My parents took care of us; they tell me now that they wouldn't be here if it weren't for me, and I remind them that if it wasn't for them I wouldn't be here. I have the satisfaction of knowing my parents are getting good care. They appreciate it… My father is set in his ways and he's hard to care for. My sisters and brothers can't do it- they'll let him have his own way. I'm not like that… I make sure he does what he needs to do to get better, so I have to set up the meds, keep track of things…" But even as Joe has been saving Medicare and Medicaid tens of thousands of dollars' worth of health care services, he has lost his own income by not being able to take on a full-time job. "My backhoe is broken down, so all I got left is my truck to earn money with. There's a lot of stress- financial stress; my brothers and sisters help some. Sometimes I can go off for five hours to do some job nearby- mom has a Lifeline that gives me peace of mind. I do carpentry,

Joseph in front of the Bateman farmhouse in the valley of Garnet Lake Road, with Crane Mountain in the distance

plumbing, handyman jobs mostly."

Caregiving for a loved one is among the most selfless acts that can be imagined. I have seen many examples of caregivers who suffered serious physical, emotional, social and financial hardships as a result. Joe is acutely aware of this. As I write this vignette Joe is undoubtedly tending to his parents' needs, with no predictable end point. "I know dad doesn't want to go back to the hospital or live out his days in a nursing home," he told me, "so I'll take care of him as long as I have to. I have no regrets- I'd do it all again, but there's times I want to take a long walk- y'know what I mean? Step back and count to ten- or ten thousand…. I still go four-

wheeling and hunting just to get away for a while. When I get back home, I know I have to keep the firewood up, the house warm- then there's dishes, laundry. You never know what you're doing from one day to the next- it's non-stop. I don't know how long I'm gonna be able to keep this place going, but we'll think of something."

Anyone who knows understands the personal sacrifices Joe is making can appreciate the determination he must have to keep going. And he hasn't touched a drop of alcohol in many years. I have great respect for the man.

Making a home visit to check on Bud Bateman

76

Photo by David T. Slingerland

RICHARD GARRETT DMD – MY UNCLE DICK

1915-2006

Sometimes I feel sorry for today's kids, many of whom have to grow up in single-parent families, often with no father. I have been blessed to have had the luxury of not one, but two fathers. Donald Way, my biological father, raised me well, giving me my love for photography and an appreciation for the outdoors, the environment and the natural world. Among many other qualities, he taught me the virtues of altruism, humility, self-reliance and dedication to family. I have been fortunate enough to have him as a parent, but I also had a second father-figure; my 'Adirondack father'. Technically he was my maternal uncle Dick Garrett, but when my parents would bring me to spend summers on Lake George with his family (my Aunt Peggy and cousins Rick and Wes) through my childhood and teen years, he treated me like one of his own sons. It was my Adirondack father who instilled in me my love of Lake George, the Adirondacks, Seneca Ray Stoddard, and his favorite author, Mark Twain. Uncle Dick taught me how much humor, literature and recreation could enhance life, and he ignited my fertile imagination. His two sons became my younger brothers, and his summer home on Lake George became our playground. He gave me a childhood that seemed scripted by Mark Twain himself- we climbed mountains, hunted baby snapping turtles and salamanders in the nearby swamps of Barber Bay, explored the lake by boat, picnicked and camped on the lake's many islands, sailed in the southern basin, went scuba diving in the narrows and off Dome Island, went fishing, slept under the stars, watched meteor showers from the dock, ate fresh tomatoes from the garden and played countless games of cribbage on the front porch. In

My uncle Dick in 2000, waving his Aussie hat at Lac du Saint Sacrement after shooting cannon at her.

short, he allowed me to experience what it was like to be a modern-day Huck Finn. For that, my dear Uncle Dick, I thank you.

In my career I have met more than my share of 'Adirondack Characters'- trappers, guides, hunters, and lumberjacks and so on. They have strong personalities, multiple talents and interests, many shortcomings and flaws, but who have a passion for all things Adirondack. They are throwbacks to an earlier time. I am proud to say that my Uncle Dick was as genuine an Adirondack Character as any. His day job was dentistry, the third generation of his family to practice it in Glens Falls. (In January 1861, his grandfather James Garrett bought a dental practice after a brief apprenticeship, only to enlist in the Adirondack Regiment at the onset of the Civil War three months later. I suspect that Jim Garrett was the father of Adirondack Characters, but that's another story (see bibliography.) My uncle's intelligence was sufficient to gain him entrance into Harvard University's Dental College where he hobnobbed with the upper class of Boston for four years before rejecting them in favor of his hometown. After practicing dentistry with his father for a few years, he went off to join the US Army as a Captain in the Dental Corps stationed in Australia during World War II. It proved to be an experience that left him with a certain swagger and worldliness as well as an appreciation for anything Aussie. After the war he returned home to the dental practice he shared with his father, whose love of music rubbed off on him. He became a member of the Glens Falls Operetta Club, and for many years his rich baritone voice serenaded local audiences, especially in the Gilbert and Sullivan productions. His interest in local history was such that he helped found the Glens Falls Historical Society, today known as the Chapman Historical Society and Museum. Along the way he was smitten by a fellow music lover and Operetta Club member named Margaret Greene, and in 1952 they married and started a family.

Although he was a devoted father and faithful husband, he had his share of faults and imperfections like any man. He could be prickly and set in his ways. He once told my wife Harriet that he and Peggy had a wonderful relationship and never fought. Knowing him well Harriet replied, "and do you know why that is, Uncle Dick?" His answer, which may have been influenced by his selectively impaired memory, was "because our marriage was made in Heaven?" She corrected him. "No, Uncle Dick, it was because Aunt Peggy was a very patient and forgiving person!" He laughed, and agreed.

Dick's greatest passion was Lake George. Except for his years in the army, he spent every summer there since 1931, when his father bought Camp Sunnyside in Pilot Knob for $2800. Dick enjoyed swimming in it, sailing on it and hiking around it. He photographed it and fished it. As a member of the Lake George Association he helped protect it. As a member of the Pilot Knob Association he helped write its history. But perhaps he is best known for his appreciation of the great ships that have passed in front of his Lake George dock since his youth. As a boy he rode the side-wheelers *Sagamore* and *Horicon*. During our childhood he delighted in taking us on the cruises aboard the *Mohican, Ticonderoga* and *Minne-Ha-Ha*. When the magnificent *Lac Du Saint Sacrement* was launched, his devotion took on a new and more unique form. The proud owner of a small but functional brass cannon, he was known to occasionally load it with black powder and fire it from his dock. He decided that it would be the ultimate expression of respect and affection to fire his cannon at the *Lac Du St Sacrement* every evening as she sailed past Sunnyside. After a while he began communicating with the ship's pilot by radio, and she would pull closer to shore as she passed so that the passengers could watch this peculiar ritual unfold. When the cannon would fire, the passengers would cheer and wave, while the pilot would blow the horn in acknowledgement. This of course gave my uncle great pleasure, satisfying his inner child. As many thousands of visitors to Lake George witnessed this aging dentist firing his salute over the years, his reputation grew. Eventually his antics were immortalized in the pages of *Adirondack Life* magazine.

My mother, who with my father had moved to the shores of Smith Mountain Lake in southwestern Virginia in 1977, recalls vividly the day

Uncle Dick sailing the Warrawee on Lake George, late 1940's

when a new neighbor moved next door. Introducing himself to my mother, he immediately noticed her Yankee accent. She explained that she was a native of New York, and at one time had lived on another lake, Lake George. Not only had he heard of it, he had seen it. "In fact," he recalled, "I took my family on a cruise on Lake George, and it was the most beautiful body of water I have ever seen. The people up there are a little strange though. We were sailing past the camp of some crazy old man, and he fired a cannon at us! What kind of lunatics do you have up there anyway?" Imagine his shock when without hesitation she turned to him and said indignantly, "Excuse me! He's no lunatic. He's my brother!!"

In the spring of 2006, after seventy-five summers on Lake George, Uncle Dick's health finally failed and he required placement in a nursing home. He found himself in the same situation that he had put to verse thirteen years earlier when the cruise ship MV *Ticonderoga*, a converted World War II navy landing ship, was scrapped. He had been so distraught at its fate that he wrote a poem in remembrance that would make Rudyard Kipling proud. He might have been writing his own eulogy:

My Adirondack and biological fathers Dick (left) and Don hamming it up at Lake George in 2002

My Last Trip

there is ' twixt men and ships that makes
d of kinship known but to those few
, and steer their course on seas and lakes,
an the years dividing old from new.

s have passed while I lay at my berth,
unger sisters came and took my place.
ine heart so strong and built to serve
rived of service, idly filling space.

t house has stared with vacant eyes
oss the waters to that busy shore,
e the throngs aboard with cheerful cries,
yful souls my decks so proudly bore!

k plates longing for the pulse of life,
ient silence have I spent the years

With memory's echoes of the sounds of strife
Of men in battle, ling'ring in my ears.

I served my country well in time of war,
In South Pacific seas, in Navy gray
I carried troops, and landed them ashore
In hostile lands so very far away.

Today my heart awoke! Once more,
With men aboard who know me, and who care,
I greet the wind and waves, just as before,
And breathe the clean and chill October air!

My work is done. I sail to meet my fate,
And leave this blessed lake I love so well.
For men and ships alike, Death sets the date,
And life must end. Let poets toll the bell!

nths later, he had left very specific instructions
hes. The majority were to be buried in the same
arents and grandparents. Another portion was

to be spread across a hill overlooking his camp on Lake George. But he had left a small portion for the most important destination of all: to be fired by his son Rick from his cannon at the *Lac du Saint Sacrement*!

FRANK LILLIBRIDGE – SUBSISTENCE FARMER

Thurman, October 1989

October 21, 1933. Twenty one years old. Received for my birthday one pair leather gloves, one dollar, one cake and five bananas, also one pair of shoe insoles. Helped to dig Hilda's grave. I had my birthday dinner at grandfathers. I have this date nine dollars and seventy-four cents. Beginning reading the Bible through, also to write it through…Saw the airplane both ways.

So begin the chronicles of Frank Lillibridge, the last Master of Maple Grove farm in Thurman. The third generation of his family to reside there, this unassuming man documented events from 1933 to 1978 in diaries that serve as a time capsule of a simple, quiet life on a southern Adirondack farm.

Frank Lillibridge at his Maple Grove farmhouse

I met Frank in 1987, when he first became a patient of mine. Our relationship grew into a friendship so that a year before he died in 1991, he generously offered to share his journals with me "for what good might come of it."

To understand Frank, you have to know the land on which he lived all his life. In the southwestern shadow of Crane Mountain, which towers like an enormous anvil over the hills between Warrensburg and Johnsburg, lies a hundred-odd acres that Frank's grandfather Horace Lillibridge bought in 1888. In those days, as is still true today, you couldn't reach this secluded area without circumnavigating Crane. The mountain was enough of an impediment to forestall the invasion of modern civilization into Thurman, a community that was first settled in the 1790s. When Horace moved his wife and six children into the two-story farmhouse built by Abner Sartwell, he found it little changed from the eighteenth century. He also found it so deeply buried in snow that he had to crawl in through an upstairs window.

Horace's second-youngest son James, born in 1880, stayed on the farm and worked it with his father. In 1912, when Frank, the only child of James and his wife Mabel was born, Maple Grove Farm was a bustling, self-sufficient enterprise.

Frank grew up in the days when muscles, not machines, performed labor, and men worked on communal projects like cutting hay. His journals vividly portray a bucolic lifestyle that echoed the farm and forest seasons. In the winter he wrote of cutting vast quantities of wood, as well as hunting and trapping rabbit, raccoon, fox, skunk, weasel, muskrat, porcupine and woodchuck. Each spring, the family tapped four to five hundred sugar maples and boiled enough sap to produce sixty to one hundred

A haying bee at Maple Grove Farm, 1916. Frank's mother Mabel is at far left, young Frank is the toddler in the left foreground holding the small hay fork and James is wearing the suspenders directly behind him

fifty gallons of syrup. In late spring they put in the garden: tomatoes, cabbage, parsnips, turnips, beets, onions, corn, string beans, cucumbers, squash, pumpkins, carrots and lots of potatoes. When summer came, they mowed hay, which they hauled into town to sell or trade. In the fall, they harvested and canned vegetables and sold the surplus; they also cut and sold more wood. The Lillibridges had dairy cows for milk and butter and raised cattle and chicken for meat and eggs. They kept horses for hauling and plowing. Mending fences, sharpening tools, shoeing the horses, hauling manure, tending livestock and taking the buggy to Warrensburg or Johnsburg for supplies were necessary year-round chores.

Time hardly seemed to touch the farm from the day Horace Lillibridge bought it to when Frank began his diaries. According to his early notebooks, the only concessions to twentieth-century convenience were a flashlight, a hand-cranked phonograph and a bicycle on which Frank had ridden more than twenty-one hundred miles by fall of 1934. In the 1950s the family bought a battery-operated radio and a chain saw. In his late sev-

enties electricity arrived. To the day he died though, the house never knew television, central heat or running water. The water source was always a spring located several hundred feet from the front door and rain barrels under the eaves.

Frank's greatest preoccupation- on paper anyway- seemed to be with wood. Just as Eskimos reputedly use a hundred different words to describe snow and Arabs have dozens of synonyms for a camel, his vocabulary was replete with nouns and verbs having to do with wood. In his 1944 journals the terms "pulp" and "wood" showed up almost two hundred times. He cut, chained, chopped, sawed, snaked, skidded, split, peeled, piled, drew, burned, traded and sold it. He logged yellow birch, white birch, basswood, ironwood, elm, oak, ash, beech, cherry, maple, popple, box elder, willow, hemlock, white pine, yellow pine, spruce and tamarack. He called it housewood, roundwood, polewood, pulpwood, limbwood, winterwood, sugarwood, greenwood, or logs, depending on its physical characteristics or eventual purpose. He measured it in blocks, cords, jumperloads, wagonloads and hitches. He cut it with Bangor saws, bow saws, Billy saws, bucksaws, crosscut saws, circle saws, Champion saws, chain saws, Lew saws, lance-tooth saws, Ottawa saws, hacksaws, handsaws, Sears saws, Simonds saws, axes,

Frank with Ma and Pa in the 1920's

adzes, hatchets, hammers and wedges. Sometimes he cut wood with one saw so he could cut it again with another.

When he wasn't putting up his own wood, he wrote about chopping it for neighbors. "I stopped at Mr. Wordens and helped him saw some wood." Frank felled trees in meadows, forests swamp, hills, valleys and along roads. His crusade against standing timber was relentless, sometimes cutting down fifty or more trees in a single day, as if he were fending off an invading army that would overrun his beloved farm. Even in his later years, when he was too old or frail to plant potatoes or boil sap, he could be found in his yard, chain saw in hand.

Frank spent the few leisure hours he had studying the Bible, going to church, writing letters, eating homemade ice cream, playing with the farm's dozens of cats, listening to records, hunting, reading *Grit* newspaper and exchanging visits with friends and neighbors. His entries show that Lillibridge holidays were simple affairs:

Monday, Dec. 25, 1933. Went up to Will Pasco's and got his wrench. We went to grandma's for Christmas dinner. We fixed the church bell. Set a coon tarp on Emma's swamp. Bought one grit and paid for next week's $.10. We got our fur check $7.75 from H. E. Galusha.

Nov. 30, 1939. Thur. I snaked some wood with Daisy. We all went to the Sanborn home and had Thanksgiving dinner. We went with Mr. LaVoilette. We had a fine time. It was the first turkey I ever ate.

Dec. 25 1962 Tues. Christmas (temp 6 degrees). A nice day. We stayed home. Pa had fire in shop and dressed two roosters. Sam and Johnnie Parker came and we shot John's new bolt .22 he got for Christmas.

Frank's prose waxed nearly ecstatic when he described his great-aunt and uncle's twenty-fifth wedding anniversary:

Mar 21 1934. Aleatha and Hazle were here. We cut sugar wood. We went to Mr. and Mrs. Cyrus Baker's silver wedding anniversary to-night. We had canned beans, salad, cake, and ice cream also lemmon ade. They had a splendid wedding cake which was served to all.

In Frank's early diaries, cash seemed of small importance. His book-keeping was meticulous, though, and in 1934 his expenses totaled $40.78 and his income was $47.75. Barter was often the medium of exchange, trading wood for kerosene, potatoes for fruit, maple syrup for grain. In many instances, Frank noted putting in a full day's labor hanging Sheetrock or repairing a sleigh for neighbor, without mentioning any compensation. In return though, friends like Henry and Winifred Wescott provided Frank with transportation to Warrensburg or even farther- that is, when they could get the car to run:

Saturday Dec. 30, 1933. Winifred and Henery came down and started the car. They had to build a fire under the car.

Jan 24 1934. Henery brought the mail. Pa hitched Daisy on to the car to get it up the hill and she broke a tug. After that Henery got the car off the road and had to go home and get his team and Winifred to get the car home.

Frank rarely left the confines of Thurman, though. His day-to-day world extended from North Creek to Warrensburg, a radius of perhaps fifteen miles from Maple Grove Farm. His first trip to Wevertown, just a couple miles past Johnsburg, was in May 1934; his first ride in a boat was in June 1948 on Schroon Lake. When he was thirty-eight, in 1950, he rode the train from North Creek to Saratoga, probably his longest, most exotic journey up to that time. In later years friends and relatives took him on day trips to such faraway lands as Ticonderoga and Vermont. More often, his locomotion was snowshoes, bicycle, wagon, sleigh, or buggy. The closest thing he ever had to an automobile was a riding lawn mower.

In some ways Frank's journals were obsessively itemized. He rarely failed to document the weather ("It came 7 ½ inches snow today") or who visited ("The Roy Russells were here except Roy" "We saw Dick's wife." "The Newtons were here.") All farm chores- even the most routine - were diligently catalogued:

Jun 6, 1945. Wed. We finished putting manure on the piece above the barn. It took eleven loads. Pa plowed the piece and I cleaned the hen house. We have drawn out 43 loads of manure. I went to the P.O. Claud and family were here this evening. They brought some bike wheels for me to fix.

June 30, 1955. I snaked out staging poles for the church with Gyp. Pa fixed chicken coop and yard, seven more chicks. I went to P.O. Got salt block. Ma canned 8 cans goat.

If Frank's bike had a flat tire, as it did six times in 1934, mention was made. When Pa cleaned the henhouse, Frank noted the occasion. He recorded each dental visit (including number of teeth pulled), every airplane sighting and any new experience: for instance, his mother ate her first banana when she was sixty-one years old. Some minutiae were truly amazing, such as "put new lead in pencil today." Frank even kept entries when virtually nothing happened:

May 8 1955. We stayed at home. Had no company. I walked up the road and back, then went to bed awhile.

A few statements went beyond my understanding altogether: "ma and I went to jasper's house and Ma burned the toad-stool Henry got in 1910." And: "Painted the east side of the rug gray."

Frank's memories appeared almost secretive, devoid of emotion or analysis. He simply recorded the day's events, often in two or three sentences. When something unusual occurred, he did not disclose personal feelings and opinions. For example, in 1945, when Daisy, his trusty draft horse, took sick and had to be put down, he wrote:

Dec. 21 1945. Fri. I went up to Henry's and he came down and finished Daisy. We went up to Billy's with Lily cow. Will came and brought the kettle home and snaked Daisy away. I went out and there wasn't any Christmas tree. It was two below zero.

His focus of attention was always on the farm. Throughout the 1940's, he never once referred to World War II. When momentous events happened elsewhere in the world, his universe remained intact:

Nov. 22, 1963. Fri. (temp 48) I sawed a little wood near barn. Chain saw quit. Pa cut the willow brush near the brook in barn yard. I went to mtn. View, put some stones under shed. I split Basswood and pine for the church shed. President Kennedy was shot and killed in Dallas Texas.

Frank's writings reveal in astonishing detail the unhurried flow of an old-time Adirondack farmer's life. As I scan from page to page and year to year, I can picture him feeding grasshoppers to the trout in the spring, eating maple sugar on snow or tuning in the radio to Billy Graham preaching from Toronto. Frank was one of the very few people I have met who seemed to have no regrets about his life. He was content to the end, and the calm complacency reflected in his 1930s observations continued through the 1970s entries.

His dear friend Edith Baker, who knew the Lillibridge family for more than fifty years, also enjoys poring over his books. "I find them very relaxing," she said. "When I read them all my troubles seem to disappear, and

Frank riding the hay wagon pulled by Gyp and Daisy past the Kenyontown Church

to the land and his parents left him little time for courting the ladies, and although he did have a sweetheart at one time, he never married. "I gave up on the idea when I got to be seventy," he told me. "I figured I'd stay single after that."

An only child, Frank was clearly the beneficiary of his parents' undivided attention and affection, and even if he never wrote it down, their feelings were reciprocated. They were always "Ma" and "Pa", and perhaps the greatest measure of his sentiment for them was expressed when they passed away. Around the time of his mother's death, in 1956 (she was sixty-six), he stopped writing for two years. When Pa died at the age of ninety-seven in 1977, Frank put down his pencil forever.

Frank came into my care in 1987 when he was hospitalized for hypothermia. One cold, rainy day he went out to dump ashes from the wood stove and fell. He had lain outside all night and was found by Edith Baker the next morning. She called Evelyn Russell and another friend, Glen Rounds, and the three of them got him into the house. "He was gray and cold as ice," Russell recalled.

Frank was taken by ambulance to Glens Falls Hospital, where he made a slow but steady recovery. The combination of bed rest and pre-existing arthritis made him very weak. Furthermore, over the years his upper back had become badly bent forward, as though the cumulative weight of all the cords of wood he had split, pounds of butter he churned and gallons of maple syrup he boiled were bearing down on him. This affected his center of gravity, making him unsteady when he tried to walk. He relied on the nurses to feed him and get him out of bed, and I was convinced that he would never return to the farm. When offered a bed in a nursing home, he said simply, "I'll be

I can travel back and forth in time and feel like nothing has changed."

Evelyn Russell, a cousin who lived nearby in what had been Henry Westcott's general store and the Thurman post office, also shared fond memories of Frank. "All the little children in Thurman used to wait for Frank and his father to go by in their hay wagon so they could beg for a ride in the hay. He dwelled in an unspoiled world, uncorrupted by TV and modern ways of conversation," she recalled. "He lived by the Bible and always remembered his mother's favorite saying, 'do unto others as you would have them do unto you.'"

Frank's lifestyle had unforeseen consequences, however. His devotion

Pa and Frank in front of house circa 1970

road became progressively narrower until I came to a sign announcing "end of county road maintenance." My route turned to dirt and gravel, with many deep ruts and washouts where small streams trickled across the path.

After several more miles of jostling through puddles and potholes, I passed Hershey Pond and the homestead where Frank's grandfather was born. From that house, Crane Mountain's summit was perfectly reflected on the surface of the tiny pond. Several steep hills later, I finally came upon henry Westcott Road and I knew I was close. I still had to ford another stream and cross an area of loose fill that had been dumped where the road had recently washed away. Finally I pulled up to a rustic little farmhouse. Its unpainted clapboards blended well with the surrounding forest, and the fragrance of wood smoke greeted me as I passed between walls of housewood stacked on the porch.

Inside, as my eyes adjusted to the dim light, I found myself in a room dominated by a huge stove, with every available space occupied by something. It was plain that little had changed here since Frank was a youngster, apart from a telephone and a knee-high refrigerator, both recently acquired. With Edith's and Evelyn's help, we got Frank into his favorite rocking chair and covered his lap with a bearskin blanket. He sat still while I took his picture, even though he seemed unable to grasp why anyone would make such a fuss over him.

After visiting a while, and satisfied that he was in good hands, I set about to find my way to Warrensburg, only twelve miles distant according to the map. In the forty-five minutes it took me to get back to town, I felt as though I had passed through a time warp. I had just spent a couple hours at a place where an enigmatic, placid gentleman had lived his whole life in isolated tranquility, and I understood why he wanted so much to stay there.

Sadly, the twentieth century finally caught up with Frank and Maple Grove Farm. In the spring of 1991 he became too weak to live alone and moved to a nursing home in Glens Falls. He died in October that year,

all right at home, and that's where I'm goin'." His friends took him back to Thurman, and thanks to their efforts, Frank not only lived there for another three years, but regained enough strength to go back to "cuttin' and splittin' a little wood," as he put it.

In 1989 he ended up back in the hospital and was about to be discharged under similar circumstances. As his doctor, I wanted to visit him at Maple Grove Farm to see his situation with my own eyes.

There's no easy route into Thurman from any direction, so I approached from the north, out of Johnsburg. I started out on a well-paved road that passed by some early-twentieth- century homes before opening into a beautiful valley with broad fields on either side, then woodlands. As I continued south, the steep northwest face of Crane Mountain appeared, looming ever closer, while the forest closed in on the other side, then both sides. The

Maple Grove Farm house in the 1940s and in 1989

two days before his seventy-ninth birthday. After Frank's death, the house was destroyed by fire, closing the final chapter on Maple Grove Farm.

I still think about Frank's home, how the seedlings of trees he cut by the thousands are silently filling in the clearing, and of a conversation we once had. "The place is a lot wilder than it ever was before," he told me, but he was at peace about that. "Did you see the big maple on your right as you came up to the house?" I nodded, recalling a giant that measured about two feet across at the base and towered over his house. "I took sap from that tree for over fifty years, and people asked me, 'Why don't you cut it down?' Well, I stopped makin' syrup when Pa got to be ninety, and I had plenty of other trees for wood. I figured somebody else might want to make syrup from it someday, so I left it for them, whoever they might be."

THE SMITH FAMILY – NEO-PIONEERS

Indian Lake, October 2010

The first time I met Andrew Smith at the Indian Lake Health Center it was for an annual bus driver physical. His appearance spoke volumes: the many tattoos, ear plugs, a braided beard, long hair, pierced nose and an English accent- all indicated a free-spirited artist who had come to Indian Lake from a very different kind of life. This turned out to be true. I also imagined him to be a loner, preferring solitude to the burdens and responsibilities of domestic life. This turned out to be *completely* wrong. As he left, I was quite surprised to see a tastefully dressed woman awaiting him, who I learned was his wife Kate. With her were two beautiful young children; daughter Macie and son Ezra. "So he's a family man," I thought to myself. "This could be interesting." Eventually, I discovered that the Smiths were even more interesting than I could have imagined.

Andrew and Kate Smith are not native Adirondackers. Andrew was born in Halifax, England; Kate was born in Birmingham Alabama. They have spent much of their lives living elsewhere in the world - Andrew in the UK and southern California, and Kate in Alabama and Virginia. They don't look like Adirondackers – Andrew's hairstyle, tattoos and English accent and Kate's stylishness, grace and hint of Southern upbringing make them an unlikely couple. It took me awhile to appreciate how well-suited they were for carving out a life in the least-populated county in the eastern United States. You might say that, because of their life experiences, they were Adirondackers waiting to happen, and they seemed destined to find each other.

At first glance, Kate's upbringing seems very different from Andrew's. As she recalls, "I think the one thing that set my family apart from most

Fred, Ezra, Vincent, Andrew, Kate, Tallulah, Nico, Arlo and Macie Smith

others was that my father was a lieutenant colonel in the US Army Rangers and served in the 101st Airborne Division. He volunteered himself for three and a half tours in Vietnam and having survived this and much more in his lifetime, he ran the house with an iron fist. Consequently, I was a very good girl who had much structure, limitations and expectations growing up. In turn I not only succeeded in scholastics, equestrianism and other hobbies, but have always been able to rise to challenges without hesitation. But I was a quiet introvert, focusing on my own interests and not giving much thought to what others thought about me." Andrew's upbringing was less structured: "I grew up in a small village and I didn't care for, or even like school as a child. But I flourished in the Sea Scouts, nearly the equivalent to the Boy Scouts in America. I started work at the age of fifteen and spent the next four years in commercial vehicles, paint and body. My father specialized in Diesel fuel injection which had a huge impact on my mechanical interests." What they had in common growing up, albeit by different paths, was the opportunity to develop self-reliance while building a diverse set of skills.

This was only part of what ultimately attracted them. They were both encouraged at a young age to develop their artistic interests as well. "I loved crafting and creating and would make lots of handmade treasures as a child," says

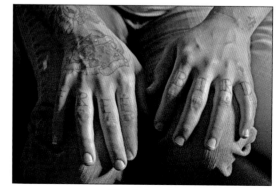

Kate's hands

Andrew Smith

Kate Smith with son Nico

worked in a motorcycle shop working on many different mechanical aspects including body work, welding, fabricating and engine maintenance," he recounts.

Kate's connection with the Adirondacks came early in life. "Before my father bought our own cabin on Indian Lake, we would vacation in the local camp grounds. I spent entire summers here and I always felt Indian Lake was a healing place, a safe place for me. My father loved it because it was far away from the conveniences of city life. And due to my father's Vietnam past, he shaped the idea in his children of Indian Lake being a place we could go to if anything bad happened. We could always depend on the animals in the woods to hunt, the wood stove to keep us warm. Our family cabin in the woods was the prelude for my adulthood." Andrew's arrival was more circuitous. "When college was done, I moved to London and squatted in an abandoned house to save rent money. I worked at a local pawn shop and as a motorcycle messenger." In his wild and crazy youth, he consumed his share of intoxicants while living a rather Bohemian lifestyle on both sides of the Atlantic. "After living like this (in England) for a while, I had finally saved enough money to get to America. I lived in a van in Venice, California for a few years with many Vietnam veterans and homeless people. It was in California that I met my first wife. I was a motorcycle messenger in LA and bought and sold motorcycles for some extra income. I used a payphone in the parking lot where I parked my van to buy and trade vehicles with other people. Eventually, I went to Hawaii to get cleaned up when I found out my wife was pregnant with our first child. We had our first son, Vincent, together and a month after his birth, we moved to Indian Lake to help her uncle with a building project. I never even knew what the Adirondacks were." His first few years in Indian Lake were difficult, as he struggled to find a home, get a job, and keep his growing family together. By the time he had accomplished the first three goals, his marriage had ended. Along the way though, he had stopped drinking, fathered four beautiful children, converted an ancient barn three miles outside of the hamlet of Indian Lake into the beginnings of a farm complete with henhouse, and begun collecting what has become a fleet of

Kate. "I loved to read, draw, take pictures and paint, and I still do many of the things I loved as a child even today." Meanwhile, Andrew's interests were not limited to nuts and bolts either: "My mother was a dressmaker and also influenced me to create things as well. Eventually I went back to college to complete a two-year associate's degree in graphic design, and completed another three years in college, minoring in photography and sculpture." If these common interests weren't enough to draw them together like two bears to a blackberry patch, they also discovered that their talents were complimentary and well-suited to living the Adirondack lifestyle. Kate could handle livestock and gardening: "My mother's best friend lived in the Blue Ridge Mountains of Virginia on a 177 acre horse/cow farm. This was where I learned to ride horses as a little girl and to work on the horse farm. We also had chickens and pigs and a small garden." Andrew could repair and operate a wide variety of vehicles: "I vehicles that now includes a backhoe, dump truck, bulldozer, two cars, a school bus, pickup truck, jeep, two all-terrain vehicles, a riding mower, two snowmobiles, two vans, and a motorcycle.

All that remained was for Kate and Andrew to meet. "I met Kate through Laura, my ex-wife," Andrew explained. Andrew and Laura had remained friendly after their marriage ended, and Laura recommended Kate as a sitter for their four children. "So Kate already knew my kids, and her uncle would come by for eggs from my henhouse. One day she came along to return a plate she borrowed the year before. I asked her to babysit as I was attending an AA meeting. She came into the house and saw the way it looked; bottles, bones, books, and it looked just like her place. We sat and talked until the wee hours of the morning and when she went home, I forgot to pay her for the babysitting, a joke we still laugh about today." Kate made it clear that it wasn't love at first sight, but rather grew over time. "I was not in the best of emotional well-being when Andrew and I first met in 2003. I had suffered a severe concussion as a result of a car ac-

Andrew, Kate and baby Tallulah

cident months earlier. It was something that physically and emotionally took a toll on my health. I didn't look so well, weighing barely 90 lbs at 5ft 9 inches- I think Andrew thought I was on drugs! He felt sorry for me so he gave me some food to take home. I ate the food gratefully that evening at my cabin and forgot to give him his plate back. Another year passed, and I returned to Indian Lake in a better state of health. I had gotten most of my life back on track and gained more weight over the year. I was trying to finish my degree in college with a nutrition/holistic healing major, minoring in cancer therapy. So, I noticed this plate in my cupboard, this unfamiliar yet very familiar looking plate. I remembered it belonged to Andrew and felt shameful for not having returned it to him a year ago. With head bowed, I returned the plate to him. I remember he was sitting on the front step of the barn with all four of his kids running about the

yard. There was something between he and I, something spiritual happening as though the forces that be were trying to tell me that we belonged together. I thought, 'Oh no! No, no, no! This was not what I had planned. I was supposed to finish my degree and not raise a family!' But I meditated for many days and felt the fear of a relationship with Andrew lift, and only the thought of he and I being friends remained. I focused on that. Once I felt comfortable with being friendly I saw some strange coincidences between us. For instance, we both collected the same odd treasures like bones, bottles, and sewing machines. We both had similar books in our libraries. He was also living a life I wanted. I saw in him something I wanted as well: peace, serenity and unconditional love for family. As I got to know him, he just seemed too familiar to me, like I had found my long lost soul mate. The pieces were fitting correctly and I just couldn't deny it. I fell in love with him and still am today. We were married in 2006." Together, Andrew and Kate have brought three beautiful children into the world, including Tallulah Sarasvati Rose Smith, the youngest member of what her parents call the Smith Tribe.

I have the greatest respect for a family that can successfully function on a limited income and the combined talents of its members in today's world. In most countries, almost forty percent of a family's income is spent on food, and twenty percent on energy. In the Town of Indian Lake, where the only grocery store closed in 2008, the average family must drive over fifty miles to Glens Falls to find a full selection of fresh produce and meat. Any family with the ability to provide fresh meat, dairy, vegetables and energy for itself would be able to re-allocate its funds toward the children's education, travel, vehicles, hobbies, etc. In the process of striving for nutritional and energy self-sufficiency, a family must work as a team toward a common goal. When the Adirondacks were first settled in colonial times,

this was the only way to avoid starvation and survive, and subsistence farms like the Lillibridges' Maple Grove Farm were the norm. With the advent of the automobile, refrigeration, cheap abundant energy and store-bought food, it became more profitable for a family to abandon their self-sufficiency efforts for paying jobs. Sadly, the new century has brought rising energy and food costs to a shrinking and aging Adirondack population, making it almost as difficult to make a living today as two centuries ago. Nonetheless, the Smith family is attempting to return to the land for most of their needs, and they are well-suited to the challenge. "We very much live in the pioneering spirit of the Adirondacks," says Kate. "Many of the things we need we make ourselves, or go without. We grow our own food in our garden during the summer, hunt meat in the fall, we harvest eggs from our chickens and need very little else to supplement our diets during the warm season. Anything left over from the garden and meat is canned for winter. But having such a large family, it doesn't go too far. We

Inside the Smith home

also do not own a dryer which helps eliminate unnecessary electrical bills. We dry our clothes on a laundry line all year round. I also make my own cloth diapers and that reduces another expense. We use hand towels instead of paper towels. Much of how we live is very practical and old school. Conveniences have been eliminated from our budget."

The Smiths have been gradually turning their sixty-five acres of land into a functioning farm, including the henhouse, well, garden, woodlot, and goat pen. Andrew has installed a wood furnace that provides both heat and hot water to the house, fueled by trees from his own land that he cuts and splits. "The best way to live off the grid is to be frugal with energy consumption," he explained. "We have a small solar array and battery backup for everyday communication and to power the outdoor wood boiler. We work on expanding the garden each year and canning more every season. We were lucky to get a deer this year, which is almost gone now. We subsist off the garden during the summer but it wouldn't get us through the winter season yet. The home-produced energy is more of a backup at the moment but we are working to self-sufficiency and that is more of a long term plan." Kate adds, "As far as homegrown foods, every year our garden gets bigger. Having the backhoe, bulldozer and the dump truck will help to open up some of the wooded lots we have that would be made into more garden area and grazing areas for our goats. We are also working out ideas on a root cellar. Andrew and I have often talked about how to utilize the mountain stream that runs through our property for possible hydro-energy and for keeping the cellar cool in the summer. Realistically, I hope that someday around 80% of our garden and wild foods will supplement our diet all year round, in the future. Eventually our goats will help bring more milk and cheese into our diets... Andrew has also accounted for the sunlight in the house when he was creating it, being sure that we had as much natural light coming into the house as possible during the day."

Life on the farm is not all work however, and the entire family seems to enjoy living the Adirondack equivalent of *Little House on the Prairie*. "Not only is it my safe place," says Kate, "it was also the place I met my husband. It has also been a place that I dreamed of raising my own children one day. My kids have the freedom to be what's natural to them, without the restraints that city life has on people. Vinnie loves snowmobiling and he has always been appreciative of nature. He loves the chickens and just the silence the woods bring to him. Fred, Macie and Arlo enjoy trapping and hunting. They love the independence and the safety that living in the Adirondacks brings to us. They know they can survive many situations that most people wouldn't have a clue to endure, like running out of fire wood in the middle of winter. In fact, I think they would rather be here than in Glens Falls. I love Indian Lake because of the people who live here, who are native here. They are some of the toughest people I have ever met, meeting many impossible challenges and getting through them. They don't depend on anyone or any institution to survive. I think my one complaint may be that winter is too long!"

"Indian Lake represents where I decided to stop roaming and raise my kids," says Andrew. "The Adirondacks feel safe to me from the rest of the world. We have a lot of different things going on, same as most people up here. I act as business support for my brother's company in the UK. We also rent our lakeside cabin out in the summer season and Kate has a sewing business. I do a bit of guiding in the spring, shovel snow in the winter and drive the school bus. I maintain and fix all our own equipment

Macie outside henhouse

Andrew comforting Ezra

95

and vehicles." Kate has learned to employ the crafts and hobbies she developed in her childhood in a new and practical direction. Using old tablecloths and other discarded as well as new organic fabrics, she has produced baby clothes, booties, mittens, diapers, and crib covers. As described in an article about her work in the November 2010 issue of *Adirondack Life* magazine, Kate is "an Indian Lake mother who wanted her babies' first undergarments to be all-natural, stitched with love, and safe for both tender bottoms and the planet."

My interest in the Smiths escalated when I realized where they live. Anyone who has driven along Route 30 from Indian Lake toward Speculator could not fail to notice a property that features a rustic barn surrounded by an armada of vehicles, a clothesline displaying shirts with letters that sometimes spell out "T-H-I-S I-S A-R-T," a wood furnace, a hen house, a fenced garden- and a four-foot wide, steel flying saucer! The saucer was preceded for years by a series of green alien sculptures standing by the roadside, arm raised in greeting to passersby. Clearly, the owner of this property had an interest in things extraterrestrial, and so I asked Andrew to explain the source of these curiosities. "I built the first alien with Vinnie for Halloween and it just got left out there," he explained. "When I eventually got around to putting it away, everyone asked where it had gone to. I've always been drawn to the possibility of aliens as a child. I remember books I read such as *Chariots of the Gods*. There are also many sightings where I come from in England, so it's a pretty normal topic of conversation there. So I fixed the alien and put him back out permanently. Then someone stole it and took it to Woodstock one year. I knew that because it had a Woodstock bumper sticker slapped across its chest upon its arrival home to us. That time we got it back intact, nothing broken. Then, another summer later, it was stolen again, and when we recovered it, it was badly damaged. Months later, we woke up to find a new alien in our driveway wrapped in plastic bags. He was about 1/4 of the size of the original alien, but it was so nice of someone to do that. We never knew who made him but we put him out nonetheless. All summer we heard honks from cars passing by to say hello to him. Many people stopped and took pictures. One night a fella stopped to talk about the space ship he witnessed. Unfortunately, the new alien was made from plaster and wasn't strong enough to withstand the brutal winter here. So, he eventually fell apart and there were no more aliens to present to the world. Later, I got around to fabricating a UFO from scrap metal. I figured if I was going to invest any more time and energy into this project, it was gonna be something that was heavy and awkward to move. It also helps that we now have our bedroom facing the UFO, with shotgun locked and loaded over the door, for the next wise guys that come around to steal it!" Fortunately, Andrew has attached the spacecraft by a thick rebar post to a block of concrete, so it is unlikely he will have to defend it anytime soon.

Although the hardscrabble Adirondack environment attracts individuals and families who want to live an individualistic and self-sufficient lifestyle, the more traditional sector of the population, primarily elderly retirees, second-home owners and

Fred, Nico, Ezra and Arlo play with the goats

multi-generational Adirondack baby-boomers, could be somewhat put off by folks with long hair, multiple tattoos and nose rings. As luck would have it, the Smiths live next door to Marion Duhaime, a retired financial executive from AT&T in her 80's who lives a quiet lifestyle in her home overlooking the Indian Lake valley.

"When I first met Andrew," she told me, "I'm going to be truthful-I didn't want anything to do with him. I would sometimes cross paths with him at Stewart's and he would always say hello to me, and I would mutter hello back as I kept moving past him. After a little while I realized he was really quite a nice fellow. He made me realize that you have to look beyond the hair, beyond the ear rings, and the braided goatee and you have to look at him as a person. He is really a gentleman. He loads my firewood because I have a wood stove, and he does a lot of other things for me. He is just a phone call away if I need him for anything. His two oldest boys, Vince and Fred, work for me raking and doing yard work and stacking my firewood. If I pay them I always get a phone call from their parents thanking me. When Andrew comes over to my house with a load of wood, we get a chance to visit for a while, and he is so interesting to talk to. He has told me a lot about the history of England and his life in California and his first marriage which ended in divorce. Andrew's relationship with the children, Kate and his first wife Laura is a wonderful relationship. They sometimes all get together for meals and its mind boggling that there is no stress or animosity and they all get along just fine. It's wonderful!"

To many people, the Smith family lifestyle might seem to represent a bizarre experiment. In reality however, it is more a re-emergence of the way people like the Lillibridge family lived in the Adirondacks a century ago. The Smiths have turned their backs on the need for the modern conveniences that almost all of us rely on, depending instead on family and neighbors while developing as many survival skills as possible. Although Andrew has a paying job with the town and Vincent has a summer job at the local movie theater, and they do use such technology as telephones and computers, the Smith Tribe know that someday they could carry on if those supports gave way, as long as they continue honing those skills.

Helena Norberg-Hodge, author of *Ancient Futures: Learning from*

The UFO

Ladakh, is a world- famous economist and sociologist whose studies of the Ladakh people of rural Tibet convinced her that-

> *…another way is possible - our search for a future that works keeps spiraling back to an ancient connection between ourselves and the earth- an interconnectedness that ancient cultures have never abandoned… in Ladakh I have had the privilege to witness a saner way of life- a pattern of existence based on the co-evolution between human beings and the earth. I have seen that community and the close relationship with the land can enrich human life beyond all comparison with material wealth or technological sophistication.*

I find it comforting to know that families like the Smiths exist, and we all could learn a lot from their ways. It comes as no surprise that they live in the Adirondacks, where survival is never taken for granted by those who haven't brought their fortune with them. It's even more comforting to see that they seem to be having fun doing it.

97

ADIRONDACK LEGENDS

here would the Adirondacks be without the foresight and talents of such legendary heroes as Seneca Ray Stoddard, Verplank Colvin, Dr. Henry Trudeau, Orson "Old Mountain" Phelps, Reverend W. H. H. Murray, Clarence Petty and all the others who recognized the unique qualities of the area, and dedicated their lives to making and keeping it that way? Certainly there would be fewer trees, more pavement, less wilderness and none of the character that makes the word 'Adirondack' invoke an image of rustic beauty, unspoiled scenery, and highly individualistic people.

Dr. E L Trudeau, pioneer in treating tuberculosis in Saranac Lake

Seneca Ray Stoddard, author, photographer and environmentalist

Adirondack literature contains the histories and accomplishments of the men and women from a bygone era, but many of these legends live on today. They are legends, at least to me, for what they have done in their lives, for the impact they have had on preserving, recording and carrying forward the true allure of the area. I have had the great fortune to meet some of these people, and provide here a sample of those whose images and stories I have collected. Some have already passed on. The rest may not consider themselves worthy of this distinction, but that only makes them typical of most Adirondackers, who just want to be part of the landscape they love and appreciate. If you meet any of them, just say "hi"- don't make a big fuss.

Old Mountain Phelps, guide and philosopher

Verplank Colvin, surveyor, mapmaker and champion of Adirondack preservation

99

CLARENCE PETTY
ADIRONDACK ENVIRONMENTALIST

Saranac Lake, September 2008

How many times in our lives do we get to meet a living legend? I'm not referring to a celebrity who may garner fame for good looks, status, or athletic prowess. I'm talking about someone whose life has been so rich in experiences and influence that his name is synonymous with the Adirondack Park. In other words, I'm talking about Clarence Petty.

Born on August 8, 1905, the chapters of his life might read as follows: Neighbor and friend of hermit Noah Rondeau, high school ice-skating champion, college graduate, trapper, hunter, woodsman, Civilian Conservation Corpsman, World War II veteran, professional pilot and flight instructor, New York State forest ranger, chauffeur for Gov. Nelson Rockefeller, Adirondack surveyor, mentor for *Woodswoman*'s Anne LaBastille, commissioner for the Adirondack Park Agency, and champion for the preservation of the Adirondack Park. To students of Adirondack history, Petty's name can be spoken with the same reverence as Stoddard, Colvin, and Trudeau. It was his detailed surveys and cataloguing of the park's natural assets that lead to the permanent preservation of hundreds of square miles of wilderness within the Adirondacks over forty years ago. His longevity is such that he continued not only flying airplanes but giving private flight lessons to would-be pilots at the age of ninety-five.

It was therefore a thrill when Marsha Stanley, a mutual friend, introduced Harriet and myself to Clarence in 2008 at his latest home at the Will Rogers Institute in Saranac Lake. I couldn't help feeling a sense of awe when I realized that I was in the presence of a man who was born when Taft was president. As I shook his hand though, he immediately dispelled my reticence with a friendly smile and twinkle in his eye. This was not a ghost or mere legend-this was an energetic, affable, charming gentleman who displayed no airs or pretense. My wife and I spent a half hour

with him and he graciously sat for an informal portrait, when there was a knock on the door. Dick Beamish and Rachel Rice, the publisher and office manager of the *Adirondack Explorer* magazine were there to collaborate on his "Ask Clarence" column in the upcoming issue. His column, where local children are invited to submit questions that allow him to expound on many Adirondack subjects, has been an outlet for his unquenchable desire to preserve and protect his beloved Park. For example when questioned about jet skis in the park in the May 2006 *Adirondack Explorer*, he said

Jet skis have no place on small bodies of water. Maybe they're all right on some of the bigger bodies of water, but I don't like them around anywhere. The damn racket is enough to drive you out. I think it would be a good idea if they were banned from all waters in the Park, because people come here to enjoy the scenery and also the tranquility, and you certainly can't do that with those damn jet skis buzzing around.

That's what I admire most about Clarence Petty- he says exactly what he thinks!

Taking our cue, we got up to leave so he could work on another of his columns. "After all," I quipped, "I don't want to interfere with your efforts to protect the Adirondacks."

"Don't worry young fella," he said smiling, "I wouldn't let you or anyone else do that!"

The year before our meeting, I had read Christopher Angus' excellent biography on Clarence. The first sentence in the book reads:

It says something about one's subject when virtually everyone contacted is bursting to talk about him. Many old colleagues and friends of Clarence's sought me out just to be able to tell me how much they thought of him.

Now I know why.

Keene Valley scene

GREG GEORGE
NYS FOREST RANGER

Blue Mountain Lake, August 2007

I like to think that Greg George and I have something in common. We are both dedicated to helping people every day, and occasionally we are called upon to save someone's life. Although he has done it in a much more heroic fashion than I do, we share a mutual respect and appreciation as fellow public servants. The main difference between us is that while I do my thing inside the Indian Lake Health Center, he gets to help people while working in the great Adirondack outdoors. Maybe that's why a part of me is just a little jealous of Greg George.

For thirty years, Greg has been the New York State Forest Ranger stationed in Blue Mountain Lake, serving the people of the Township of Indian Lake that stretches from North River to Blue Mountain Lake. To those of us who know him, Greg epitomizes all that is good and noble in a forest ranger, and almost every year-round resident of Indian Lake and Blue Mountain Lake recognize his chiseled physique, rugged good looks and bright red truck. His presence commands respect wherever he goes, and during his long career, there are very few places in his territory he has not gone.

A native of Voorheesville New York, Greg has always liked the outdoors. After four years at Cortland College and a one-year career as a high school teacher, he had a change of heart. "I realized that teaching in a classroom wasn't for me, so I enrolled in the New York State Rangers School in Wanakena," he told me during the summer of 2007, "where I earned an Associate Degree in the Forest Technician Program. Working outdoors was what I wanted to do, and I've never looked back." His first six years as a ranger was spent in Otsego County near Cooperstown, but all the while he had his eye on the Adirondacks. "I was looking at the Adirondacks for the search and rescue, fires and 'big-woods' type of experience." In 1977, he found it in Hamilton County when two rangers, Gerry Husson in Indian

Lake and Don Perryman in Blue Mountain Lake, retired. Greg replaced both of them. Moving into the ranger's home on the shore of Lake Durant with his wife Jean, they raised son Joel and daughter Maggie while Greg literally became part of the landscape he seemed born to protect.

As a frequent user of the state's many trails in Greg's territory, I find it a comfort to open the sign-in log book and invariably find that the first entry reads – *Greg George – on patrol*. Clearing blowdown, helping injured hikers, and enforcing the state's laws are all part of his patrol duties. During the winter when the forests are relatively free of human encroachment, he straps on his snowshoes, grabs a brush and gallon of paint and 'paints the line', marking trees that form the hundred-odd miles of boundaries between private and state land in his territory. "A lot of times, the lines haven't been painted in thirty to forty years. You use the old maps and look for the blazes or old paint on the trees, which are sometimes hard to find. Then as I paint the trees I take GPS readings, especially at the corners of boundaries. I enjoy it; you can really appreciate being alone in the forest at a time when it's more open. It's a great time to be outside. It can be almost spiritual, and it's great exercise too."

In the spring, he finds himself helping the many local rafting companies prepare for the hugely important white water rafting season, a major source of income for the local population. It is also a time to   repair and replace lean-tos, clear debris from campgrounds and maintain other infrastructure.

During the busy summer and hunting seasons, he is more apt to be dealing with men behaving badly. The caves and dangerous rock formations of Chimney Mountain on the outskirts of Indian Lake in particular are a lure that some male adventurers find irresistible. Right after the Great Blowdown of 1995, he had to help rescue a man who had fallen off the top of the thirty-foot volcanic 'chimney' into an impenetrable tangle of broken trees, shattering both legs and several ribs. After taking hours to cut through the blowdown with chain saws and pull the man out on a lit-

The "chimney" on Chimney Mountain

ter with ropes, his radio call for a helicopter was denied due to approaching thunderstorms. "It was a long, painful carry down, but he made it," Greg recalled. "He was stoic too. The only time he screamed was when the ambulance crew had to straighten his broken legs out before we put him on the stretcher." Ouch!

Barely a year later, Greg found himself back on the same mountain to rescue a man who had crawled into Eagle Cave only to pull a five-hundred-pound slab of rock down on himself, which pinned him on his back with barely space underneath to breathe. It took hours for Greg and a crew from the Indian Lake Fire Department to carry huge amounts of rescue equipment up the mountain and carefully lift the rock off the man in a tiny space using ropes, levers, a crowbar and all the muscle ten firemen could muster. "He was lucky," Greg told me. "The only thing he broke was his collar bone, and he was able to walk down the mountain." Blue and Snowy Mountains are also common trouble spots for him.

When I asked him to recall the dumbest thing he ever saw anyone do, he laughed. "It's funny to remember now." He proceeded to tell me a story right out of the Darwin Awards. It was the opening day of hunting season about twenty years ago and the weather was cold, windy and snowing. There were two hunters across Lake Durant from Route 28, not far from Greg's home. For some reason, they couldn't figure out how to find their way around the lake, and they were disoriented, cold and scared. They decided to start a fire, but they had trouble lighting it in the wind, so they burned all their money trying. When that didn't work, they decided to build a raft

to cross the lake toward the highway, which was in plain sight across the lake. They somehow tied several logs together, climbed onto the raft with their guns, and struck out for the other side. Of course the raft fell apart, dumping both men and their weapons into the cold water. One decided to swim across the lake, while the other was left stranded soaking wet and freezing where he had started. "About 10 o'clock at night," Greg continued, "my brother, who happened to be camping at the Lake Durant campsite, knocked on my door. 'I think you better come with me', he said. 'I thought I heard someone calling for help.' We went out in his skiff and found this guy across the lake suffering from hypothermia and brought him right to my house. We took him into the basement where the wood stove was, stripped him down and warmed him up. Meanwhile, Jean was upstairs with the other guy who had been picked up by a motorist and dropped off. He was thawing out in the bathtub!" He also recalled having to search for and rescue the same elderly, deaf, lost hunter three years in a row. When it comes to people doing really dumb things he explained, "Almost always, alcohol is the root of it all."

As human behavior has become more irresponsible, law enforcement has taken over a larger and larger role in Greg's long list of responsibilities. "A number of years ago the DEC made a change where we (rather than the State Police) became the sole agents providing law enforcement for the state in the campsites. So now, on busy holiday weekends, we are confined to staying in and around the campground areas to provide law enforcement in lieu of some other police agency, instead of having the freedom to go into the more remote areas. We have to take care of things like domestic violence, drunkenness, vandalism and other things that you don't like to see in the great outdoors." Greg can serve lawbreakers with tickets much like a state police trooper. He is now licensed to carry a 9 mm semiautomatic pistol, and he knows how to use it. Although meant to be a part of his police ensemble, he is happy to say he has never had to wield it for that purpose. "I do find it useful for dispatching injured deer and moose that have been struck by cars though," he admits.

The inside of Greg's 'mobile office'

When not patrolling the woods, Greg and his fellow field rangers can be found on the road in their heavy-duty trucks, which are their offices on wheels. As Greg showed me the inside of his vehicle, I was amazed at what he could fit inside. He had a chain saw, axe, hand saw, wet suit, ropes, pulleys, come-alongs, camping gear, rakes, fire clothing, toolbox, boots, pumps and hoses, climbing gear, trail markers, maps, ticket books, food, water, gasoline, oars, and paddles, as well as two canoes on the roof. And that's just what I could see. He is in constant radio communication with a dispatcher both in the truck and by hand radio during the day, and by phone at night.

For the past thirty years, if you were lost, injured, or stranded in his territory, chances are that Greg George was the man who found and returned you to civilization safely. He has participated in approximately fifteen rescues per year over that time, and estimates that he has climbed Blue, Chimney and Snowy Mountains at least 150 times each. Now, however, as I write this, he is planning to retire in 2010. For twenty-five of those years, especially on a beautiful summer or autumn day when I was sitting at my desk in the Indian Lake Health Center coping with piles of paperwork, I have occasionally found myself wishing I could trade places with Greg. I could be out in the woods painting the line, or helping to find a lost hiker. Maybe I could bring my Nikon in case I happened to encounter a beautiful landscape. But that would mean that Greg would be sitting behind my desk, doing what I do, and somehow I don't think he would appreciate that. When I learned of his planned retirement, I was actually surprised that he wanted to step away from such a dream job. He invited me to join him at the weekly Liars' Club coffee klatch at the Blue Mountain lake firehouse one Tuesday morning to explain.

So what makes him ready to leave, and what won't he miss? "The phone calls at all hours, especially in the middle of the night for something that is not life threatening," he replied.

Now *that* I can understand!

Indian Lake from Baldface Mountain

REV. E. PAUL MILLER
BAPTIST MINISTER

Indian Lake, October 2008

One of the most satisfying aspects of my career has been the pleasure of providing medical care to the people of Indian Lake. Over the past decades, I have come to appreciate the well preserved sense of neighborliness and community spirit that exists in this tiny hamlet of twelve hundred people. Yet because of its remoteness and its aging population, the town is struggling to maintain itself as a functioning, self-sustaining community. Thankfully, there are a number of remarkable individuals, some native Adirondackers and some from elsewhere, who take it upon themselves to serve as the social glue holding the town together. The four churches in Indian Lake play a vital role, providing social and spiritual support to residents of all ages in a grass-roots way that adds to the 'retro' feel of this special place. All the local clergy are actively involved in the ambulance squad, meals-on-wheels, youth programs, and much more. At least one of them carries this dedication well beyond the confines of the Adirondack Park in a way that truly defines who he is.

Reverend E Paul Miller, or Pastor Paul as he prefers, came to Indian Lake by chance. Born in New York City to the son of a minister, he spent his youth in places like Buffalo and the Finger Lakes region. He became interested in missionary work as a young man, spending time in the Bowery and Harlem, where he was not always welcomed. While in his early teens he became interested in foreign missionary assignments and began this work in Puerto Rico. He met his future wife Shirley while at language school in Costa Rica. By his early twenties he found himself in Argentina, and he has been returning there regularly ever since. I asked him what made Argentina so special to him. "I spent two and a half years there," he once told me, "and our daughter Julie was born in Argentina. Latin America is something I have in my heart." When Julie was found to have congenital heart problems, Paul

and Shirley were forced to come back to the United States for her medical care. After spending three years in Cincinnati and four in the Adirondack hamlet of Wilmington, the Millers were drawn back to Indian Lake where they had briefly lived in the Baptist mission house as newlyweds. They have continued to spend two or more weeks in Argentina every year even as their appreciation for this Adirondack town has grown. "We are blessed to have the best of both worlds- literally", he said.

Pastor Paul is a man of faith in more ways than one. When he goes to Argentina, it is not to bask on the beaches or relax in fancy hotels. "Sometimes I spend weeks in the high Andes ministering to the people of Indian descent," he explained to me in 2008, "but I spend most of my time in the poorest sections of Buenos Aires, especially a neighborhood called 'Fort Apache'". It's named after the movie *Fort Apache, the Bronx* where an entire neighborhood is beyond the control of the police. It is a lawless and largely godless place. "The police won't go there and the army has sealed off the perimeter. Somewhere between 22,000 and 80,000 people live there, and there is tremendous need for almost everything. It's a human cesspool of illegal immigrants, gypsies, the forgotten and the jobless, many of whose minds are so blown out with drugs, glue and alcohol that they are in a hopeless condition. They live on tea, lard bread and bone soup. But I try to show them that God loves them, to give them some hope."

Knowing that robbery and kidnapping for ransom were common in the region, I asked Pastor Paul how he could remain safe, and still accomplish anything in such an environment. "I bring things with me that the people can use there," he replied. "People down there don't care how much you know until they know how much you care. I'm not going to ram the gospel down their throats; I want to show them that the Lord loves them. Last year I brought 42,000 doses of Advil. A few years before I

brought a huge duffel bag full of used soccer shoes. I tell them 'silver and gold I have none but such as I have I give to you.' It's an exciting life putting everything on the line. One of the motivations is to see people whose lives have changed as a result. When I brought the soccer shoes down I was told never to get into a gypsy cab at the airport in Buenos Aires. I had heard that when you get into a gypsy cab, you never get to where you're going- you get robbed instead. At the airport I was approached by a gypsy cab driver, who was very insistent that I use his taxi. I flatly refused but he would not give up. Finally, after no other cabs were available, I got into his cab with my soccer shoes. The first thing he asks me when

The Reverend reaching out in Argentina

Pastor Paul outside his Indian Lake church

we are moving is 'what do you have in the bag?' I answer 'I have soccer shoes'. 'What do you have soccer shoes for?' he asked. 'Because God loves people and I love people and I brought these shoes down for these people.' He asked me to explain more about this, and by the time we arrived at the hotel he said 'this is what I need in my life!' He asked the Lord to forgive him and to save his soul and then he drove off after giving me his name, address and a list of people who needed help. Four years later I met him again. His taxi was clean and polished and he thanked me for giving him hope in his life."

Pastor Paul had many other similar stories as well. I asked him if he had been physically threatened during his visits to Fort Apache. "Oh yes", he replied matter-of-factly. "I've had people try to stab me and throttle me with wire…. But I've had a lifetime of the Lord protecting me. I feel I'm immortal until God is finished with me. I'm doing his work, so if he wants me to keep doing it, he better keep me alive! Right now I have a basement full of down jackets, and I can stuff about forty-five of them into one duffel bag. I hope to bring them to the rural communities that I visit in the high Andes, near the Bolivian border."

The rest of the year he spends much of his time helping the young people of Indian Lake with an international organization called AWANA ("A Worker And Not Ashamed"). "It's an interdenominational program for kids from ages 3 to 6 that does not preach the Baptist doctrine. But we do look for a spiritual quality in our children, and using competitive games we teach sportsmanship, teamwork and character development. We also have a program for teenagers on Tuesday nights where we fill a bus with about two dozen kids and go to Northville where we join about one hundred kids from other Adirondack communities to play basketball, videogames and other activities followed by a half-hour message from the gospel. On the way home we stop for Chinese food, which the kids love. Many kids come from broken homes or have reading disabilities, ADHD and so on. We have our hands full, but that's an opportunity, not an obstacle. I hope the program will allow these young people to appreciate where they live, and give them a reason to stay in the community when they are older."

Pastor Paul takes great pride in his engaging and enlightening sermons. "I put a lot of work into my sermons, and the people know that. I do my homework, and I certainly don't wait until Saturday night." His optimism is perhaps his greatest strength. There is even a rainbow over the front door to his parsonage! Anyone who passes by the First Baptist Church on Route 30 in town looks for the inspiring weekly messages that he displays on the marquis out front. "We want to show that we care for the people who are lost, confused or need an uplift." Some of them are amusing, such as "Without the bread of life, you are toast". Others are more profound as the pastor explained. "On one occasion I had put a message out that had to do with God giving us hope, and that Sunday I was approached by a woman who had been driving out to Sabael where she was planning to take her own life. She told me 'When I saw that message, I turned around and went home. It seemed to be meant for me.'"

Not content to save lives and souls by spiritual methods, the good pastor has also saved a life with his bare hands- none other than an Indian Laker named Elmer Norton. He recounted a spring day over twenty years ago when he was invited to go rafting down the Hudson River with some other Indian Lakers, including Elmer Norton. "As we were getting into the raft, I happened to pick up one of the straps that are used to lash the rafts onto the bus roof. For some reason I still can't explain, I had the forethought to tie myself onto the raft with it. On the way down the river, we went over a small waterfall at Blue Ledge, and Elmer went over the side into a hydraulic (whirlpool) below the falls. He was sucked under the water, and every few seconds he would bob up to the surface for a second before going under again. He was not coming out of that trap, so I timed his appearance so that the next time he bobbed up, I jumped in and grabbed him with both arms and we were pulled up by the others in the raft. Without that strap, neither one of us would have survived. It was a miracle." "He sure saved my bacon!" Elmer later confirmed.

I always enjoy my office encounters with Reverend Miller. His optimism is infectious, and I always try to do what I can for him. A few years ago, he was having problems with his left hip, and X-rays revealed significant arthritis. He was limping noticeably and he was concerned that it would interfere with his next mission to Argentina. At one point I suggested that he might be best served by letting me refer him to an orthopedic surgeon, but he deferred. "Let me work on it for a while," he said with his usual sanguinity. "I'll call you if it doesn't improve soon." He began riding a bicycle around town, and the next time I saw him he was walking normally with essentially no pain. I remember being pleasantly surprised, but he wasn't. "I had faith that it would get better so I could return to Argentina on time," he said. Another miracle perhaps?

If everyone had Pastor Paul's faith and buoyancy, the world would indeed be a better place. He has reminded me that there is nothing more important than having hope for the future and being able to enjoy life's simple pleasures. In fact, I find myself quoting one of the messages I once saw in front of his church that read:

"The best things in life aren't things"
Amen to that!

NATHAN FARB
PROFESSIONAL PHOTOGRAPHER

St Regis Mountain, September 2007

During the summer of 1985, Nathan Farb's dazzling book *The Adirondacks* was published. It was the most important book of Adirondack photography to appear since Eliot Porter's *Forever Wild: The Adirondacks* was published in 1966. It captured the grandeur of the landscape as no one had since Seneca Ray Stoddard, the legendary Glens Falls photographer of the late nineteenth century. At the time, my photography exploits were limited to using Harriet's Minolta SRT-201 35 mm camera to take pictures of our son Andy and his little sister Emily. Although I had fantasized for years about buying a medium format Bronica ETRS camera and photographing the Adirondack landscapes I saw on my daily commute to work, I couldn't justify the expense to take the next step. When I learned Nathan Farb was to appear at a book signing at a local mall, I felt I had to meet him. Perhaps he could provide me with the inspiration I was looking for.

As he signed a print of *View South over Clear Pond from Sunrise Mountain* for me, I mentioned my own amateurish interest in Adirondack landscape photography. He looked at me thoughtfully, his passion for the topic prompting him to discuss the subject in an analytical way even with a total stranger.

"What do you do for a living?" he asked.

"I'm a family physician practicing in the southeastern Adirondacks," I replied.

He considered this for a moment. "That's both an advantage and a disadvantage," he said with a skeptical look. "Your income level will permit you to afford to take as many pictures as you want, but it will

The master at work

be tough for you to find the time to do it the way I have been able to. Do you have a family?"

"A wife and two terrific kids" I said proudly. He winced perceptibly.

"That makes it a lot tougher yet. How are you going to get away from your work and family long enough to get up into the Adirondacks for hours or days at a time?"

"My main chance will be when I'm going to and from work between Glens Falls and Indian Lake and during vacations when we hike as a family" I offered dubiously.

His expression said it all, but with as much tact as he could muster, he gamely replied "good luck".

On an impulse, I asked one more question. "Do you have any words of wisdom for a photographer in my situation then?" I queried sheepishly.

To my surprise, there was no hesitation in his response. Looking me in the eye he replied, *"Always have faith in yourself, even when no one else does."* Maybe he says that to all the would-be Stoddards that ask for his counsel. After all, it is not bad advice. But it struck a chord with me, perhaps because it was the kind of encouragement I was looking for. I sold my baseball card collection from the 1950's and 1960's, invested the money in the Bronica system and never looked back.

Although I didn't realize it at the time, Nathan's advice was given with all of the gravity of a man who had learned the lesson himself- the hard way. Eleven years later, I read an excellent biography of Nathan in *Adirondack Life* magazine by his friend Alex Shoumatoff that revealed a life far more complex than I had imagined.

The product of Russian Jewish parents who had emigrated to Oklahoma, Nathan's father had committed suicide three months before he was born. He lived the first four years of his life with his grandparents in Arkansas, until his mother married a rabbi who moved them to Lake Placid at the end of World War II. He learned from his stepfather what it took to make a living there. "My stepfather was the Adirondack Rabbi," Nathan told Shoumatoff. "He was the part-time chaplain for the tubercular veterans at Sunmount (Infirmary), in Tupper Lake. He stitched a living together, just the way most of us do, from a bunch of pieces. Up here you can't make a living doing any one thing." Growing up in the central Adirondacks, he was exposed to both the beautiful landscapes and the anti-Semitism that was common there. At thirteen his life was upended once again when his step-father died, forcing his mother to move the family to Hackensack New Jersey. He eventually enrolled at Rutgers University, where he gravitated to the urban scene of the early sixties. "If there was anything I aspired to, anywhere I saw my escape, it was in the world of artists and intellectuals," he said. Scraping together an income working in the hotel business, he went on to study psychology at Temple University, served in the army, settled in Manhattan's East Village, and bought his first camera. Surrounded by the fertile but tumultuous atmosphere there, he taught himself how to use his Pentax with the mentoring of Diane Arbus, the renown *avant garde* New York photographer. Arbus inspired him to use the camera "as a tool of discovery, as a scientific instrument, like a microscope or a telescope." Nathan produced a body of images that captured the spirit and turmoil of the sixties in New York City in the tradition of such social photographers as Arbus and Walker Evans. By 1971 his success led to an appointment in the art department at Rutgers as an instructor in photography and mixed media. That same year he also became a father, which was a bittersweet experience when his daughter Esme was found to have cerebral palsy.

The Rutgers University appointment allowed him to travel to Eastern Europe, including Siberia, as part of a cultural exchange program, where he produced a powerful portfolio of portraits that was eventually published in five countries in a book entitled *The Russians*. After his position was eliminated eight years later, he found himself in Bowling Green Ohio, helping Esme's mother Judith Treesburg care for her while Judith attended graduate school. The flat terrain was so depressing that within a year he began to feel the pull of the Adirondacks, and he returned with the plan of documenting the 1980 Olympics. But, on arriving back in Lake Placid, he rejected the commercialism, which he had always found repulsive, and sank into a great depression. He could have given up, and almost did, but the natural beauty of his surroundings and his creative instincts saved him. As he told Shoumatoff many years later, "Nature has always been my best friend. It doesn't belittle you. It doesn't hurt you. Your lovers will leave you, your faithful dog will up and die on you, but nature is always there. What it's really about is yourself. You never escape yourself. I realized that wherever I go, I have to take me along with me, so I'd better get along with me..." He disappeared into the forest for a week, and the decision to produce a major photographic portrait of the Adirondacks came to him like an epiphany. "I decided to do something for my children so that even if I died- and I was so depressed that I had considered packing it in- they would know where my heart really was." It took five years of work and rejections by every publisher he could find until Rizzoli, an Italian producer of high-quality art books, decided to take a chance on timing the book's publication with the 1985 centennial of the Adirondack Park. It has been a huge success, and for a generation, as Shoumatoff said, "Nathan could be proud of having defined the photography of the Adirondacks." Perhaps more importantly, *he never gave up on himself, even when everyone else did.*

The next time I met Nathan was almost twenty years later. My first book was out, and we were both participating in the Chronicle Book Fair in Glens Falls in October 2005. His third book *Adirondack Wilderness* was about to be published. This was a dream come true for me; I was sitting at a table with Nathan Farb on one side of me and Anne LaBastille, the legendary author of the *Woodswoman* series on the other side. Nathan was very gracious and complimented me on my book. "This is very important stuff you're doing," he said. "You should keep it up!" More words to live by.

On a beautiful autumn weekend in September 2007, we met again when we were invited to the home of our friends Tom and Marsha Curley on Upper Saranac Lake. The Curleys enjoy bringing together people of Adirondack interest for stimulating conversation and outings, and we were invited to enjoy the fall foliage along with my wife Harriet and Nathan's long-time friend Kathleen Carroll, New York Daily News film critic and Chair of the New York Film Critics Circle. Nathan caught me up on his latest exploits, juggling his time with Esme in Washington DC and his efforts to find a publisher for his manuscript of *Summer of Love*, a retrospective photo-essay of his 1960s Manhattan street photography. Nathan brought a portfolio of his finest color prints, as well as his famous Deardorff 8" x 10" view camera that had captured all his exquisite, high-resolution images over the previous quarter century. He admitted he had not taken the camera up an Adirondack summit in more than ten years, and it was easy to see why. It was the size of a small television and with its tripod, lenses and film magazines, weighed almost forty pounds. At sixty-six and with some arthritis, Nathan had 'gone digital', as had every other Adirondack photographer I know, which instantly reduced his equipment burden by about thirty-five of those pounds.

But when Marsha suggested we climb St Regis Mountain, with its breathtaking views of the Saranac Lakes and St Regis Wilderness area, the temptation to use the Deardorff was irresistible. Fortunately, Tom McDermott, a friend of the family, was more than willing to carry the camera system on his back up the mountain, and as a result, we enjoyed a magical day.

Nathan was in his element. Deploying the Deardorff, he disappeared under a black hood, wrestling the camera into position by turning the various knobs on the bellows and tripod. Shoving in a film magazine the size of an Adirondack phonebook, he once again filled his enormous ground-glass focusing screen with a beautiful Adirondack landscape.

As Nathan captured the memorable image, his enthusiasm was contagious, and it infected the rest of us as we understood what the experience meant to him. As he explained to me later, "...the camera almost becomes a part of my body, much like a bass fiddle player and his instrument...the hard work is staying attached to the world with one side of the brain (watching every shift in light and clouds) and yet using the other side of the brain to calculate exposure and framing… (it is) a very female act, allowing something to come into you and through you." Viewing Nathan through my own camera, I caught that familiar feeling of joy unleashed by the creative process as I photographed him at work. Even with his head obscured under a shroud and viewing him from behind, Nathan's body language said it all- in that moment he was in a world of his own; there was not another person on the planet.

Later as we made our way down the mountain I reminded him of the words of inspiration he gave me over twenty years earlier, and how much they meant to me. "You told me to keep the faith, and so I have," I said. Smiling back at me, he replied "I'm glad you did."

Me too.

Nathan and his trademark Deardorff view camera

PETER HORNBECK – TEACHER & BOATBUILDER

Olmstedville, November 2008

July 4, 2008 was a beautiful day on Blue Mountain Lake. I had just bought a Hornbeck Black Jack canoe from Peter Hornbeck's boat shop in Olmstedville, and I was eager to take it for a test run. It was a picture perfect day, with cirrus clouds dancing across an azure sky, while a light breeze stirred up the warm summer air. There are few things in this world that are more enjoyable than paddling a small boat across an Adirondack Lake, an endeavor that combines aerobic exercise, refreshing water, and breathtaking Adirondack scenery. I had been enjoying my fifty-pound Perception America kayak for seven years, but found its weight a hindrance. Now as I glided effortlessly across the water toward Eagle Lake in my eleven-pound, carbon-fiber canoe with the trademark red stripe running its length, I noticed John Collins, the former Chairman of the Adirondack Park Agency and Director of the Adirondack Museum approaching me in a small motorboat. Nodding appreciatively, he called out "nice boat!" Gliding past The Hedges to my left, three attractive young ladies were paddling toward me from the historic resort. As they crossed my bow, the lead paddler called out "I like your boat!" Seeing she was paddling a Hornbeck Lost Pond canoe, I realized that my Black Jack wasn't just a well-designed vehicle to carry me over the waters of the North Country; this was bling, Adirondack style! I also realized I owed all my paddling pleasure to Pete Hornbeck.

Pete, like so many other successful Adirondackers, is a man of several talents who re-created himself eighteen years earlier in order to make a living in this economically unforgiving area. A native of western New York State, he had earned a teaching degree from the University of Buffalo before serving in the US Army during the Viet Nam War. After receiving postgraduate education at Geneseo in 1969, he began a 22-year career as an elementary school teacher in the Johnsburg Central School in North Creek, teaching kids ranging in age from eight to eleven years. As far back as 1970 he had an almost instinctive interest in experimenting with the construction of small, lightweight boats. "When my Dutch ancestors came to this country," he explained to me in

Peter in his boat shop

115

Hard at work on St. Regis Pond

a medical leave of absence for a year, spending much of his time tinkering in his boat shop. He rediscovered the reason why he came to the Adirondacks in the first place- its flowing water. "White water was always my big thing. I always wanted to live in the Adirondacks, and teaching started out as a means to an end. It became more than that, but having a heart attack at age forty-nine made me realize that I needed to make some changes in my life. The inflexibility of teaching rankled- I didn't have time for anything else. Now I was enjoying the freedom- a lot!" He began building boats full-time, and he found what had been missing in his life- the need to create something with his own hands that he could share with others. He also discovered he could make a living doing it, which made everything in his life fall into place.

His craftsmanship is not limited to his boat building- he is also a talented self-taught artist. Studying the technique of Winslow Homer, his watercolors reveal the depth of his connection to his surroundings. But his boats are what have made his name a legend in the Adirondacks. I already appreciated what they

the summer of 2009, "their name was changed from *Hoonbeek* to Hornbeck. *Hoonbeek* is Dutch for 'village by the river'. I guess it's in my blood." He began experimenting with fiberglass, then Kevlar and later, carbon fiber; trying to create the perfect boat for the waters of the Adirondacks. It began as a hobby, then morphed into a part-time career as his boatbuilding abilities became known to the many avid paddlers in the area who were searching for the same ideal craft that he was. His life changed course abruptly in 1991 when he felt a pressure in his chest while jogging. "Go figure," he recalls: "The only jogger in Olmstedville has a heart attack!" As it turns out, it was a blessing in disguise.

"Teaching was hard to beat," he reflects. "You've got your summers off, and you're working with kids whose minds are still open to all kinds of things. Being a part of the community and watching the kids grow up- that part was fun. But there was always something missing." He took

represented- a means of escaping the ordinary to experience the extraordinary. With the distinctive red stripe along the sides, one could do it in Adirondack style. "That red stripe was my wife's idea", Pete confessed. "One day Ann told me she didn't like the way my yellow Kevlar boats looked. 'They look like a urine sample!' is how she put it. So I asked her what I should do about it, and she said 'I think you should put a red stripe along the sides.' The rest is history."

Peter now reigns over a small kingdom in Olmstedville, and Ann is unquestionably his queen. His two workshops, warehouse and guest cabin sit between his sales office and "Lake Inferior", a small pond where customers can test-paddle his boats. His home and barn are found elsewhere on the 100-acre complex, where he sponsors fund-raising parties and environmental conferences when he is not designing a new boat or working on a watercolor. He generously donates his canoes and artwork to worthy causes, while overseeing the production of approximately four hundred boats every year. "…and I never get tired of seeing my boats around, people using them and enjoying life," he admits. Over five thousand of his craft ply the waters of the world, and he has sent boats as far away as Sweden. Yet he prefers to keep his business small and personal, with only five loyal employees and no plans to expand. "The way it is now, Ann and I can manage things without too much stress. I could easily expand, and wholesale my boats to other retailers. I could hire more workers, open another store or two and sell a lot more boats- but then it wouldn't be fun anymore." As it is, a visit to his shop on Trout Brook Road in Olmstedville is like a pilgrimage for those of us who appreciate what he does and how he does it. If there is such a thing as an Adirondack paddler's boutique, his store is the model.

Peter is now so seamlessly entwined into the landscape he likes to paint that the name Hornbeck has become a trademark for what makes the Adirondacks such a special place. And all because of lifestyle changes triggered by a myocardial infarction. There's a lesson in there somewhere- perhaps Peter Hornbeck's teaching days aren't through just yet!

Pete admiring his handiwork on Little Clear Pond

PATRICK SISTI - ADIRONDACK GUIDE

Duck Hole, July, 2011

Peter Hornbeck still remembers the first time he ever met Patrick Sisti: "I don't know this guy at all. He comes into my shop looking for a boat. One thing leads to another- he likes to fish, as I do. I bring him into my house to show him my watercolors I'm working on. There's one of a fisherman wading into a river. He's holding onto a stick to keep his balance. So I'm showing Pat the picture. He looks at it and he looks at me and he says 'Frankly, it looks like a blind guy with a staff waiting for a bus!' There were several people in the room and the room goes quiet, while I digest what has just been said." Peter laughs as he recalls "Then Pat breaks the silence- he looks at me and says: 'Not everybody likes me!' He's totally honest." That would be Patrick- the rare example of a man who says exactly what he thinks.

Patrick, who was born and raised in Brooklyn, explained his connection to the Adirondacks. "My father bought 1600 acres of land in the Town of Indian Lake in 1942, a year before I was born. He brought my mother to the land with a picnic basket and a bottle of whiskey, and they celebrated under an apple tree. I was born nine months later! My father always called me 'the apple of my eye.'" His father built a two story fieldstone house with a knotty pine interior. The caretaker of his father's property, Leroy Spring, looked after it when the Sisti family was at their primary residence downstate. Patrick loved the man he called 'Uncle Leroy'- "He taught me everything I know about the Adirondack woods. He was the image of everything I considered manly. He was my hero- my mentor." As his physician, I had the pleasure of knowing Leroy for over twenty years, and it explained a lot about who Patrick was.

In 2009, Patrick introduced himself to me at the Chronicle Book Fair in Glens Falls and we seemed to connect immediately. Aware of his reputation as a skilled guide, and noting his flowing, shoulder-length hair and humble demeanor, I was immediately reminded of Bill Nye, the legendary guide of Seneca Ray Stoddard. In 1878, Stoddard immortalized Nye and his fellow guides with word and portrait. (Nye Mountain is one of the forty-six High Peaks):

...a more honest, cheerful and patient class of men cannot be found the world over... skilled in all the lore of woodcraft, handy with the rod, superb at the paddle, modest in demeanor and speech, honest to a proverb... The wilderness has unfolded to them its mysteries, and made them wise with a wisdom nowhere written in books.

Patrick Sisti paddling his beloved Hornbeck Black Jack

The timeless Adirondack guide

These words could have just as easily applied to Patrick. His physical presence, intellect, sense of humor, and his skills with all manner of camping, fishing, canoeing and cooking made him the modern incarnation of the classic nineteenth century Adirondack guide. When he invited me to go on a camping trip into the Adirondacks the next summer, I could not refuse, even though I had not been camping since my six-year career as a Boy Scout had ended over forty years earlier. Perhaps he sensed that there was something missing in my busy life as a physician, and that he could re-connect me with my younger self.

Having a few months to prepare for the trip, I read one of his humorous fly-fishing columns in the *Adirondack Explorer*.

The Secret Society of Adirondack Pond Fishermen is so secret it doesn't even know it exists… but it does. You've seen us in the trailhead parking lots… You've met us on the trails going into an Adirondack Pond or coming out….We usually don't speak to you. If you ask us a question, we'll usually grunt or nod and look in a different direction. We're fearful of the questions you'll ask: "What pond you going to?" or "Catch any?" When that happens, we go comatose. Our faces frost over. Our eyes glaze. We begin muttering and pawing the ground like a buck in rut. Congratulations: You just found a member of the Secret Society of Adirondack Pond Fishermen.

By the time we got down to planning our first camping trip, the project had expanded to include other like-minded men: Peter Hornbeck, whose boats we would be using to traverse the various ponds we would explore; my 27-year old son Andy, who had already climbed half of the Adirondack High Peaks; Dan Berggren, the renown Adirondack songwriter and musician; and Len Constantineau, a chimney sweep by day and an avid gardener and pond fisherman in his spare time. When we finally convened in July 2009 at Peter Hornbeck's boat shop, Andy looked around and announced "I feel like I am going camping with the League of Extraordinary Adirondack Gentlemen!" We have called ourselves that ever since.

Every summer since, we have made memorable outings to visit such hallowed Adirondack waters as Saint Regis Pond, Little Clear Pond, Lake Henderson, Upper and Lower Preston Ponds, Duck Hole, Tupper Lake, the

Patrick and Peter planning our maiden voyage in April 2009.

Bog River, Hitchins Pond and Lows Lake; places I might never have seen in twilight and in the early morning light if it had not been for Patrick.

Patrick was Hornbeck's greatest fan, and loved Peter's boats. In the Explorer, he wrote:

When I reach (a) pond, I used to look for two things. The first is a campsite where I can put up a tent… the other is that elusive Adirondack pond boat, usually hidden a few hundred feet away in the woods….Nowadays, I have a Hornbeck "Black Jack" that weighs under twelve pounds. I carry it on my shoulder. I don't need no stinking pond boat.

The last time I went paddling with Patrick was September 12, 2012. I had the day off and I had just won a rare Hornbeck red Kevlar modified New Trick canoe in a raffle and was eager to take it for a ride. We met at his Indian Lake cabin and headed up to Long Lake in his Prius, Hornbecks lashed to the roof.

Soon we were paddling our way up the lake, basking in a beautiful late summer sun as we passed such landmarks as Oven Point Camp, Round

120

Dawn on Lake Henderson

121

Island and Watch Rock, where we turned back. After three hours we had returned to the town beach, where Tom Helms, who operates one of only two remaining floatplane services in the entire Adirondacks, agreed to fly us over our most recent camping destination on Lows Lake. (You can watch a video of our flight on You-Tube. Look for "Takeoff from Long Lake with Pat Sisti"). It was a great day!

A few weeks later I was stunned to receive a call from Patrick's nephew, Gary Sisti, who sadly informed me that Patrick had collapsed suddenly and died on the shore of Long Pond as he was returning to his car. "My dad passed away when I was fifteen," Gary told me, "and I am the oldest of eight kids. Patrick stepped up to be a father figure, a big brother and an uncle all rolled into one. He's been a constant in my life since my earliest memories of him when we summered together in Indian Lake as kids."

I console myself with the knowledge that Patrick was doing what he loved best when he was stricken, and he will never know the ravages of Alzheimer's disease, cancer or any of the myriad afflictions that we all fear. Yet anyone who knew him feels cheated out of future meetings and outings with a uniquely generous, charming and infectiously jovial character. Patrick Sisti was truly an Extraordinary Adirondack Gentleman. Here is one last bit of lore from the CEO and chairman of the Secret Society of Adirondack Pond Fishermen:

A few negative items about Adirondack ponds; There could be a foot or two of mud on the bottom. Why do you think so many are called Mud Pond? Essex County alone has 11 Mud Ponds. Old-timers, when asked for their favorite trout water, would reply "Mud Pond" and walk away snickering. Me, I'm different. I don't mind telling you my favorite ponds. Some of them are Shannon's Pond, Tyler's Pond, Emily's Pond, Pup's Pond, and Andrew's Pond. Of course, those aren't the real names. Those are the names of my grandchildren.

Patrick's photo of me in my Red Rocket on Long Lake

ADIRONDACK PHYSICIANS

As a young, green physician working in the Glens Falls Hospital's emergency room right out of residency (before embarking a year later on my life's work as a rural Family Physician in the Hudson Headwaters Health Network), I would see the patients of the local physicians at all hours of the day and night. Looking back, the primary care physician that impressed me the most was Dr. Richard Hogan of Hudson Falls, New York. The son of a Washington County dairy farmer and a farmer himself in his spare time, Dick and his wife Betty were able to bring eleven children into the world, all of whom have grown to be successful and productive members of society. He practiced medicine his entire career in Hudson Falls, a blue collar community that for decades was the home of many employees of the General Electric plant along the Hudson River, while also caring for the many dairy farmers who live in Washington County. He took care of babies while also caring for their parents and grandparents. He learned how to practice medicine before there were computers and elaborate radiology and laboratory studies, developing the best physical diagnosis skills of any physician I have ever known. Equally impressive was his memory. It was truly photographic.

One night well after midnight, I was evaluating a rather unkempt and uninsured man in his forties with chest pain whom I was convinced needed to stay in the hospital for further evaluation. When I asked him if he had a doctor, he identified Dick Hogan as his primary care physician.

"When did you last see him?"

"Oh, I'd say 'bout ten years ago."

"Ten years?! If he hasn't seen you within the last three years then technically he has no legal obligation to take care of you. I can call the doctor for unassigned patients- at least he will have to agree to admit you."

"Doctor Hogan will take care of me" he said with conviction. My skepticism must have been obvious, since this was not an individual who would be pleasant to take care of, especially since he had no means of paying for his care. "He's known me since I was a kid. Why don't you give him a call in his office right now" he suggested. "He'll remember me- I know he will."

"It's one o'clock in the morning!" I replied with exasperation. "I'm sure he's home in bed asleep. You expect me to wake him up when he's not on unassigned call? He won't appreciate that!"

"Just do it. I guarantee he'll be my doctor."

At this point it was hard to say which one of us was more annoyed, but I figured that when I called his office and no one answered, I could at least prove this man wrong. I dialed the number, and to my amazement, Dick Hogan answered it on the second ring. I was so surprised, I was momentarily taken aback. "Hey Dick, what are you doing there at this time of night?"

"Seeing patients-what else?" he answered matter-of-factly.

"You always see patients this time of night?" I asked out of ignorance. Apparently I had a lot to learn about this man.

"If you had eleven kids, you'd be here too!" he said with remarkable humor, considering the late hour. "What have you got for me?"

"A guy you haven't seen in ten years who has no insurance. I'm sorry to lay this on you but he insisted you'd know him and agree to take care of him. If you don't want to I'll give him to the doc on call- just say the word."

"What's his name?" Dick asked.

When I told him, Dick immediately recounted the man's age, medical history, family history, place of residence, names of acquaintances, as if he was a member of Dick's family. He even remembered the right bundle branch block on the man's EKG that I had been worried about. "He's had that as long as I've known him. Ask him if he still drinks two pots of coffee and a six-pack every day." The man answered in the affirmative with no surprise in his voice. It was I who was astonished that Dr. Hogan could recall such detail.

"He probably has another esophageal ulcer like he did the last time I took care of him. Go ahead and get him a bed. I'll see him later on this morning."

I learned a lot about Doctor Hogan that day. I learned the fact that, until I could match his ability to know patients on both a medical and personal level, I had no reason to consider myself anything special. After thirty-some years of trying, I'm still not there yet.

As a way of putting my professional experience into perspective, I find it helpful to read the autobiographies of physicians from an earlier time. Though many have been published, my personal favorite is *Tales of a Country Doctor*, written in 1939 after a fifty-two-year career in upstate New York by Dr. James Holley MD. (Dr. Holley's son was my grandfather's dental school roommate in 1910.) When my mother passed the book down to me, I was fascinated to read about his 1884 medical school training, including a recollection of his final exam:

> *…we were taken in sections of ten students before four professors for an oral exam… The first question asked me was, "What is colic?" I replied that we have several different kinds of colic; bilious, renal, flatulent, etc. This answer seemed to satisfy him and he passed me on to the next professor.*
>
> *My second question was: "Suppose you were called to see a patient who was unconscious, how would you make the diagnosis?"*
>
> *"If," I replied, "I could not rouse my patient I would decide it was a case of apoplexy. If I could rouse my patient I would decide it was a case of hysteria."*
>
> *He said, "Not always, not always."*
>
> *Then I qualified my statement by adding, "If my patient was an elderly person, I would decide it was apoplexy and if young or of middle age, especially female, I would decide that it might be hysteria." That answer seemed to satisfy him and the other two professors did not examine me."*

JAMES A. HOLLEY, M. D.

It seems hard to believe that early in his career, there being no cars, he traveled by horse, train or carriage to the many house calls he made, many in the dead of winter:

> *One bitter cold night on a journey to a patient out in the country, I took a driver along in order that I might be able to sleep on the way. Suddenly it got very warm around the region of my feet, and I awoke with a start. In my sleep I had tipped over the lighted lantern which had been resting between my feet. The oil had run out and had caught fire, igniting my robe. I threw the lantern and robe into the road. Fortunately, the only damage done was the slight scorching of my trousers.*

One wintry night I was called to a farmhouse about six miles from the village, to attend a sick baby. I had a driver on this occasion also. The snow was already very deep on the ground and slightly crusted. As we started out it was still snowing, the wind was very bitter, and driving conditions were anything but ideal. I covered my head to protect myself from the wind. We had gone some distance when the horse stopped. It was so cold that the snow was freezing the driver's eyes shut. He said, "We'll never make it. Let the child die!" But somehow, knowing we must answer the call of a sick baby, we managed to get through the storm to the farmhouse. When I went inside to examine the child, I found him, a very young baby, sleeping naturally, with good pulse, normal temperature, and every indication of good health. My questions revealed that he had been crying a little in the late afternoon, and the mother was afraid he was going to be sick. I was not too kindly disposed toward that family as we started out to battle that storm again for the six long miles back to the village.

Many of the common diseases Dr. Holley saw, including typhoid, smallpox, tuberculosis, cholera, trichinosis and eight foot long tapeworms are now rare or extinct, at least in rural New York. Others, such as strep throat, pneumonia and erysipelas, could be life-threatening in the days before antibiotics.

As his career evolved he made use of such modern technologies as the automobile, telephone, surgery, anesthesia, and, finally, early antibiotics such as sulfa and penicillin. By the time his medical career was winding down, he had witnessed the dawn of modern medicine.

In my own career I have seen the development of countless medical 'miracles' that have revolutionized the practice of medicine. Ultrasound, CT and MRI reveal images of the human body in extraordinary detail. Powerful drugs have made great inroads in the control of infectious diseases, cancer, anemia, heart disease, diabetes, hypertension and mental illness. Surgical, endoscopic, robotic, and imaging-guided procedures now exist to stop bleeding, restore blood flow, repair arteries and joints, remove stones and tumors while avoiding open incisions, which reduces suffering and speeds healing. Telemedicine and the internet have allowed near-instant access to medical records, physician consultations and clinical infor-

mation. Thanks to US Senator Charles Schumer, we even have broadband high-speed internet access in tiny Indian Lake, making it possible for me to access records from Glens Falls Hospital and download the latest medical information. In many ways, Doctor Holley might envy the tools I have at my disposal.

I would have to caution Doctor Holley to be careful what he wished for. There is also a dark side to the practice of modern medicine which has decreased both physician and patient satisfaction. I wonder if medical legends such as Dick Hogan and Mac Depan that I feature in this section would approve of the depersonalized, assembly-line care that characterizes 'modern' medicine. An insidious and relentless force has so invaded the industry that it is pushing many physicians, nurses, physician assistants and office staff toward an early retirement. It is of course the bureaucratic infrastructure, insurance company demands, and the relentless paperwork of "managed care".

There was a time when paperwork was seen as a necessary part of medicine practice. It was limited to writing orders, prescriptions, progress notes, and dictating letters, hospital admissions and discharge summaries. Although time-consuming, such paperwork served a useful purpose in documenting the information necessary for the care of a patient. With spiraling costs of our modern medical miracles and some spectacular cases of medical fraud, it now requires insurance company paperwork to have patients see specialists, undergo surgery, obtain medical equipment such as oxygen, hospital beds, walkers, prosthetics, and take certain medicines. Health insurance companies took paperwork torture to new levels by denying hospital admissions that they thought were too long or unnecessary, so that they could avoid paying the hospital for the services rendered. This requires me to create detailed and time-consuming letters of appeal to justify the need to hospitalize a patient. With the advent of the electronic medical record (EMR), most 'paper' work is done electronically, but this has only made it easier for insurers to demand it faster and in larger quantities.

Things only got worse as the cost of prescription medications escalated. Insurers responded by punishing physicians who prescribe a necessary but expensive drug by demanding information on the patient's diagnosis and what other (cheaper) drugs had been tried before they would authorize its use. Sometimes the insurer would force me to use a cheaper drug, even if it was less effective. Patients of course suffered but not insurance companies, and this only dehumanized the process of prescribing medications even more.

As the threat of malpractice lawsuits has increased, we physicians are often forced to practice defensive medicine, ordering unnecessary tests and specialist consults in order to confirm that a condition does not exist. This approach generates more prior authorizations, referrals, test reports and costs, ratcheting the paperwork burden up another notch. One can only wonder if Doctor Holley would be willing to trade his 1939 practice for mine under these conditions.

He might have reacted the way Dr. Charles Van Gorder did. Tom Brokaw, in his wonderful book *The Greatest Generation*, profiled this heroic surgeon whose practice began in the 1930's, just when Dr Holley's was ending. Dr. Van Gorder actually volunteered to participate in the D-Day invasion of June 6, 1944, allowing himself to be hauled across the English Channel with his medical staff in a flimsy wooden glider which crashed into a tree, splintering into pieces upon landing. Unfazed, he and his team set up a mobile operating room right in the thick of the fighting, saving countless GI's even as they faced great danger. After an illustrious military career he came back to the United States to establish a hospital in rural North Carolina where no medical care had previously existed.

Brokaw described the impact that the 'dark side' of modern medicine had on his career:

> *In the early days of his…practice, his patients often paid him with produce from their garden or fresh-killed game. When that gave way to distant bureaucrats rejecting claims because a code was entered improperly, or dictating care instructions, Dr. Van Gorder's enthusiasm for what he loved began to fade. A man who began his career operating behind the lines and in the line of fire, a physician who learned more in a week of combat than an insurance clerk could know in a lifetime of paper shuffling, had little patience for the system that was overrunning his love of medicine.*

Over the years I have come to know and respect many primary care physicians and specialists. I have chosen a few, whose stories have left a particular impression on me. They could just as easily have been included in the "Legends" chapter, but our common profession compels me to give them their own section. What they all have in common is compassion, dedication, humility, vast experience, common sense, and a sincere desire to help their patients live healthier, better lives- all essential qualities for the modern-day physician. They epitomize all that is noble in their profession. Plus a few quirks…

Lake Abanakee, on my commute to the Indian Lake Heath Center

JAMES MORRISSEY – CARDIOLOGIST

Glens Falls, 1999

It's hard to do anything for fifty years. Practicing medicine for fifty years is almost impossible. Practicing a sophisticated, high-tech specialty like cardiology for fifty years is unimaginable. Meet Dr. James Morrissey, whose picture I took in 1999 to honor his 36th year in medical practice. That was fourteen years ago, and he is still practicing cardiology today, fifty years after completing his cardiology fellowship in 1963. To anyone who does not know Dr. Morrissey, the obvious question would be- "why?" Those patients and fellow physicians who know Jim *do* know why.

Born and raised on a farm near Medina in western New York State, Jim's medical journey started with a simple childhood insight. "I didn't know what I wanted to be when I grew up, but I knew I didn't want to be a farmer, so I sort of backed into it." He chose Cornell University for his undergraduate education, and at the suggestion of his advisor, subsequently applied for admission to the University of Rochester School of Medicine. His experience with patients and faculty during his internal medicine residency attracted him toward a fellowship in cardiology. In the meantime he met his future wife Kay Higgins, a native of Glens Falls. Although he was offered practice opportunities in Rochester, his rural upbringing made a community like Glens Falls seem much more attractive. Asked in 1999 if he had any regrets, he didn't hesitate. "Absolutely none. It's been a great place to raise my six kids. I learned to ski with them, and I still love it here. The school system, the large and sophisticated community hospital, and the beautiful environment have made it a great life for me."

When he began treating heart diseases, there were no statin drugs for cholesterol, no beta blockers, ACE inhibitors or calcium channel blockers

Jim Morrissey, Glens Falls Hospital Coronary Care Unit, June 1999

to treat hypertension, and very little evidence-based medical knowledge about how to treat common conditions such as congestive heart failure, coronary artery disease, and atrial fibrillation. The learning curve over the last half-century has been steeper than the Adirondack cliffs of Wallface Mountain, yet he endures. "Despite all the medical discoveries I've seen in my career," he told me, "there has been a tendency to depersonalize medical care more. Sometimes I think we get ahead of our technology, and I think the art of practicing medicine has suffered. Even so, I think my patients are still appreciative; they value our relationship, and so do I. I'm more interested in the patient contact than in the high-tech procedures."

His long-term patients still speak of him with reverence. When I asked one patient that Jim and I shared why she liked him so much, she replied, "He's just…*nice*! He listens to you, and he cares what you think. He doesn't just care about my heart, but the rest of me as a whole person. I feel very comfortable with him, like an old family friend." This is a recurrent theme among the many patients who continue to seek his cardiology care. They know that every decision he makes is based on their specific needs and circumstances, rather than on some abstract and impersonal formula. He treats people with respect and humility, and they notice. Patients that I want to send to a cardiologist will often say, "I've heard Doctor Morrissey is very good. Can I see *him*?" When I ask why they want to see him, they usually recall comments from friends and relatives about how well he treats them as *people*.

When I remind Jim of all the frustrating changes forced on physicians by managed care and the state and federal governments, he nods patiently. "You have to learn to adapt and adjust in medicine, just as you do in any other profession," he says. Having earned more than enough income over his career to support his family and his modest lifestyle, he and Kay have become significant benefactors to the Glens Falls community. Not content to limit altruism to Jim's day job, the Morrisseys have generously supported many regional projects that include the Glens Falls Youth Center, the city library, hospital, symphony, YMCA and theater.

In the end, the reason that James Morrissey is willing to endure the increasing demands made on the modern physician after fifty years is actually very simple- *he enjoys helping other people.*

"I would still encourage anyone to go into a career in medicine if that's what they really want to do," he told me. "It's still a great way to spend one's life…. I really enjoy what I'm doing, and I'm not really ready to give this up." He told me that fourteen years ago!

Crandall Park in Glens Falls, near Jim Morrisey's home

130

HARRY "MAC" DEPAN MD – LEGENDARY SURGEON

Queensbury, 2006

How does one measure the success of a surgeon's career? Is it by the number of lives saved, or the number of years of good health added to the lives of the surgeon's patients? Perhaps it is the number of years devoted to performing surgery, or the average number of hours per day or days per year spent in the operating room? How about the number of personal sacrifices made by that surgeon during his career?

By these yardsticks or any other you can think of, Harry McCarthy "Mac" Depan's surgical career has been an unqualified success. His rough-edged, direct no-nonsense manner made him a favorite with his patients, even as his intelligence, courage and skill with a scalpel make him a legend among his peers. For over forty years, Mac devoted his life to the surgical care of his patients. It cost him a marriage and a portion of his left ventricle, which only temporarily slowed him down. Perhaps one small measure of his patients' affection for him was displayed when a man on whom he had just performed successful surgery donated $40,000 in Mac's name to Glens Falls Hospital. When he finally retired after a 42-year career, the party in his honor had to be held at a convention center to accommodate all his admirers. No surgeon in or around Glens Falls, before or after, is held in quite the same esteem as Mac Depan.

Now, at the seasoned age of 83, Mac has reluctantly put down his knife and is able to reflect back on his life. He recalls his average workday starting with rounds on pa-

A reflective Mac Depan in his Queensbury home

tients at Glens Falls Hospital at 6 AM, operating into the afternoon, then office hours, then back to the hospital for evening rounds until 9 or 10 PM, then home to a late dinner and bed. This was his schedule seven days a week, fifty-one weeks a year for decades. For many of those years, the only vacations he took were to the annual American College of Surgeons (ACS) conventions which were held in various cities across the country. Like many of his contemporaries who grew up in the 1940's and 50's, he relied on the stimulating effects of nicotine to help get him through the day, with little attention paid to proper diet or recreational exercise. He spent so little time at leisure that, despite a very keen and curious mind, he knew relatively little about the arts, computers, literature or any of the finer things in life. Although he has always enjoyed watching basketball and football, he did not allow himself to be distracted by such things until his retirement. But even now, if you put him in front of a computer, the first thing he wants to do is log onto Web MD!

In the summer of 2006 I spent an afternoon with Mac in his Queensbury home to catch up on things since his retirement, and listened to him describe his surgical lifestyle in his typical matter-of-fact way. When I asked him whether he would be willing to live that life over again, he didn't hesitate. "Yes, and I'd do it all over again in a minute. I always enjoyed what I was doing- it was fun! I was always happier in the OR than in a movie theater." I think that to understand what motivates Mac it helps to realize that medicine is practically encoded in his DNA. His father was a general practitioner and anesthetist, his former wife and daughter are head surgical nurses, his son Harry is Chief of Cardiothoracic Surgery at Ellis Hospital in Schenectady, and as of this writing his grandson Cormac Depan is a surgical resident at Albany Medical Center. One of his earliest memories is as a five-year-old in 1928 riding a train to New York City with his father to pick up a state-of-the-art anesthesia machine that would replace the nineteenth-century open-drip ether technique, which was invented during the Civil War. Growing up as a headstrong youth in Glens Falls and spending his summers at the family property on Indian Lake, he developed a level of self-confidence and fearlessness that would serve him well in the OR. "One of my high school friends was a hockey and lacrosse player named Ned Harkness," Mac recalled, "who got me interested in lacrosse. We formed our own club and played private schools, and it was a very physical game." (Ned would go on

to become a hockey coach for colleges such as RPI and Cornell before moving to the Detroit Red Wings organization.) Graduating from Glens Falls High School in the summer of 1941, he enjoyed the last summer vacation he would experience for more than a half-century.

Determined to pursue a medical career as his father did, Mac went to Williams College for undergraduate studies, and then on to medical school at Cornell, completing both within six years. While a freshman at Williams, Pearl Harbor was attacked.

Father and son, 1945

"That was pretty much the end of my childhood", he recalls wistfully. As an undergraduate during World War II, young Harry enlisted in the Navy as a cadet in the U-12 training program, where future physicians could receive medical training in the military in exchange for tuition assistance. By 1943 he had completed his undergraduate studies and was assigned to the US Naval Hospital in Brooklyn as an apprentice seaman until returning to medical school where he received his medical degree in 1947.

After three years of surgical residency at the Hartford Hospital in Connecticut and the Hospital for Special Surgery in Manhattan, he was still in the naval reserves in 1950 at the onset of the Korean War, and was called up to serve in an Army MASH unit. "There were so few surgeons in the Army in 1950 that naval surgeons were assigned to Army field hospitals," he explained. Recalling the movie and photographic images of wounded young American GI's crying for help in a chaotic war-torn environment, I asked if it was anything like the MASH series. "Yes, and it was a great learning experience….. I enjoyed it!" His only regret was that General MacArthur was not allowed by President Truman to drive the Chinese out of the entire Korean peninsula when they had the advantage. As he put it, "If they had listened to MacArthur, we wouldn't have a psychotic Elvis impersonator running North Korea like a concentration camp right now over fifty years later."

Just before leaving the Navy in 1952, Mac met his wife-to-be Betty Natter, head surgical nurse at Chelsea Naval Hospital in Boston, while removing a gallbladder. Was it romantic, I asked? "Hell no!" he replied. "I stepped on her @*#!! foot, but she ended up marrying me anyway!" By the time he established his surgical practice back in his home town of Glens Falls in 1954, he had received general and thoracic surgical training in Hartford, Boston, New Jersey, and Houston. His father, who was still practicing general medicine in Glens Falls, welcomed Mac home. He hit the ground running. "Things were a lot different in those days," he said pensively. "There weren't so many people then. You got to know everybody. There wasn't the paperwork. You could run the office with two girls-now you need a hundred!" He described the days when general practitioners doubled as anesthetists in the OR, administering anesthetic gasses through inflated Foley catheters before the modern endotracheal tube became available. Drawing on his training and experience, he could do almost anything with a scalpel. "In a small town like Glens Falls, a general surgeon in the 1950's could do all kinds of stuff." Over his productive career Mac removed countless diseased gallbladders, appendices, upper and lower intestines, lungs, thyroid glands, ovaries, uteri, larynxes, lymph nodes, spleens, breasts, kidneys, stomachs, tonsils, arms and legs. He removed leaking aneurysms, repaired perforated ulcers, drained inflamed pancreases, and replaced broken hips. One of his most difficult cases involved a man who was impaled on a metal fencepost in an industrial accident. The pole pierced the left chest wall, tearing through skin, muscles, ribs, lung, arteries, veins, and the pericardial membrane surrounding the heart before exiting below his shoulder blade. "The toughest part was controlling the bleeding enough to see what I was doing," he recalled as if it had happened yesterday. "I had to remove two lobes of his left lung and he took at least ten units of blood, but I got the pole out and he survived. It missed his heart by less than a half-inch!"

My own most enduring memory of Mac in action was when I paid him a visit in operating room 2 at Glens Falls Hospital one day in 1989. I had sent him an unfortunate woman named Lenora whom I had seen two weeks earlier for abdominal pain. A rather massive woman, she had been treating the problem herself for months until it became intolerable, and finally came to me with the admission that "I was afraid if I came to you, you'd find something really bad and I would have to go to the hospital and have surgery." When I laid my hand on her abdomen, the look on my face must have said *I have found something really bad and you will have to go to the hospital and have surgery.* Her belly felt like a rock and it was obvious that she had advanced ovarian cancer that had already spread throughout her entire abdomen.

Lenora's only chance for surviving even a few months was to have radical surgery to remove the pelvic organs and as much tumor mass as possible before undergoing aggressive chemotherapy. After CT scans and blood tests confirmed the diagnosis, I brought her back to explain the situation as frankly as I could. After receiving a great deal of handholding and encouragement, her first question was, "Do you know any surgeon who can do the kind of operation I need?"

"Only one," I answered.

I arranged for her surgery to be done by Mac on a day when I would be on duty in the hospital. As I entered the operatory, Lenora's surgery was well underway. The floor was covered with bloody sponges and Mac's hands were a blur of movement. "How's it going Mac?" I asked. Pulling his head out of her abdominal cavity, he reached behind him to grab the contents of the specimen basin, holding up an enormous, unrecognizable mass of diseased flesh that must have weighed ten pounds. In his typical bat-

Mac Depan in the Navy

tlefield bravado he declared, "Well, Danny, I'm either gonna kill her or cure her!" Somehow, after several hours of painstaking dissection, he had managed to remove the uterus, ovaries, a section of small intestine with overlying omentum, and innumerable nodules of tumor that had cemented the entire mass together, and free it from her abdominal cavity. Amazingly, not only did she survive the surgery and the chemotherapy, but she enjoyed almost twelve years of good health before dying well into her seventies of an infectious disease. For the rest of her life, Lenora, a devout Catholic, worshipped the ground Mac walked on and prayed for him every week at mass. He apparently visited her Indian Lake home several times afterward to see how she was doing. No doubt there are many thousands of others who owe a similar debt to this amazing man, who can still seemingly remember every operation he ever did on anyone and why. Yet to him, these deeds seem no more noteworthy than those of the postal worker putting mail in a mailbox.

Eventually, the single-mindedness that goes with total dedication to his craft began to take its toll. First, his marriage to Betty, frayed by the relentless demands of a busy surgeon, came to an end in 1981 after their children had built lives of their own. This only made him work harder. In April 1985, he gave in to an impulse to invite a lovely surgical nurse named Martha Belisle that he had known for some time to go skiing in Vermont. "He didn't even know they skied in April when we went", Martha recalls. "We were so nervous we forgot to buy lift tickets before we got on the chair lift!" They have been together ever since.

The next life-challenging irony in his life came in 1992, while defending his decision to put a small access road into his Warrensburg property to the Adirondack Park Agency in Ray Brook. "Because I had a couple of ferns near my pond," he explained, "they said it was a wetland. As I was making my argument, I developed a terrible pain in my chest. I knew immediately I was having a heart attack!" Although he was eventually able to return to his work and Martha, his heart had clearly taken a blow. This legendary surgeon finally had to slow down. He started assisting his colleagues in the OR as he gradually closed down his own practice. He began socializing a little more.

It was during one such social occasion with Martha four years later, while enjoying a dinner with a physician colleague at a local restaurant, that Mac almost entered the 'eternal care unit'. "One minute Martha and I are enjoying a nice dinner with my friend (and physician) Cloyd Kerch-

ner and his wife Lynne, the next I'm in the coronary care unit at Glens Falls Hospital looking at Jim Morrissey. I had gone into ventricular fibrillation and collapsed. Martha and Cloyd had to do CPR on me until the squad arrived, and they shocked me back to a normal rhythm. If Martha and Cloyd hadn't been there, I'd have been a dead pigeon. Now I have an implanted defibrillator and pacemaker." This near-death experience had a great impact on Mac, but not in the way it is portrayed in the movies. "There was no white light for me to go toward," he confessed. "I decided that I had better enjoy myself while I was still alive, for whatever time I have left. Frankly, I didn't expect to live this long!"

Of course, Mac's idea of a good time after retiring isn't the same as yours or mine. At first, he had no interest in golf or other recreational pursuits. Instead he devoted himself to missionary work through the American College of Surgeons where he could still do surgery, but without all the paperwork, malpractice concerns and billing issues. After closing his office, the first setting for his new life chapter was Mogadishu, the civil-war-torn capital of Somalia. "Mogadishu made my years in the MASH unit look easy," he recalled. "I doubt there is a worse rat-hole anywhere on earth, and they were desperate for surgeons. We weren't there to teach the locals how to brush their teeth- there was a war going on. There were guns going off all the time, and there were hundreds of young men and even kids all shot up…. We had to do dozens of amputations without general anesthesia. We used ketamine (a tranquilizer) to sedate and relax them. It worked pretty well." Describing it today, he might have been recalling a vacation where it had rained a little too much. From there, he went to other places in need of his abilities, including months in Kenya, Saipan, and six trips to Guatemala. Although spiritually and emotionally rewarding, the physical toll was significant. "I can't do it anymore," he admits ruefully.

Fortunately, after twenty years Mac still has the devoted support of Martha, who is not only an experienced nurse, but, more importantly, his portal to the world that he missed out on for so many years. She has opened his eyes to the previously neglected concepts of recreational travel and wintering in exotic tropical places. In 1986, while visiting an old friend's winter home on Saint Eustacius in the Dutch West Indies, Mac was persuaded to buy the adjoining one-acre lot. Over the next two years he built a spacious villa on a hill overlooking both the Atlantic Ocean and the Caribbean Sea, and for the last twenty years he and Martha have spent the winter months there. This summer (2006) they are booking a cruise to Europe where they plan to visit Barcelona, Venice, Rome and Monte Carlo.

"You must be excited…." I suggested.

He shrugged. "I'd still rather be doing surgery!"

"That's your favorite thing in this world, isn't it, Mac?"

"For a lot of my life, it was almost the only thing."

"So, what's your least favorite thing in the world then?"

"What I'm doing right now- sitting on my ass!!"

You've gotta love him! Mac Depan represents a vanishing breed of physician whose life has been almost entirely devoted to his craft, and that devotion has earned him the ultimate accolade. It is expressed in many different ways by the thousands of people who owe their lives to Mac. I still remember how Lenora put it: "Doctor Depan is a saint in my book."

Indian Lake Moonrise from Depan Property

DANIEL O'KEEFFE II – RETIRED OBSTETRICIAN & TENNIS CHAMPION

Queensbury, May 2008

When North Creek's Owens House Gallery opened in 2004, I was honored to be the first artist to exhibit there, and I chose to display many of the portraits and landscapes that would become part of my first book, *All in a Day's Work*. I was hoping for a good turnout, and when a few people began to trickle in, I busied myself showing them around and discussing my work. The atmosphere remained fairly subdued for the next half hour when suddenly there was a flurry of sound at the entrance and a sizable group of people entered the gallery. I heard an instantly recognizable voice announce: "We're here, so the party can start now!" Smiling, I turned with delight to see a handsome, silver haired man with a beautiful young woman on each arm, followed by an entourage of North Creek's most renowned citizens. Dr. Dan O'Keeffe II had entered the building. At that moment I knew the evening would be a success!

Dr. Dan is not a man you can ignore, especially in North Creek. He personifies the charm, history, and rustic nature of "the Crick" better than any man alive, and he is proud of his roots. Born there in 1921, he treasures the many memories of his youth in this quintessential Adirondack hamlet.

In those days the people in our community had little of material things, but they all had faith in God, love of their families, respect for their neighbors and a willingness to work. They strictly adhered to certain principles, such as personal responsibility, honor, commitment, loyalty, hard work, faith and family… It was a wonderful place to grow up, even during the roaring twenties and the terrible thirties. We lived a great life with our close knit family and friends. Social life was simple, revolving around church, sports, school, lady's bridge games, men's beagle trials, turkey shoots and hunting, fishing and camping.

He has preserved these memories in the several books he has written- required reading for anyone who wishes to know what it was like growing up in the Adirondacks in the early 20th century. His recollections could almost be mistaken for the life and times of Tom Sawyer. Describing a contemporary whose birth records had been lost, he recalled "some neighbors used to claim that he wasn't born, but hatched out from under a stump behind the barn." In his day, a road now known as Ordway Lane was a dirt path near a pasture commonly known as "Cow Turd Avenue." Like Tom Sawyer, young Dan and his friends were always getting into trouble.

One character we visited from time to time was Charlie Pereau. Charlie had a monkey in his garage on Main Street, and we would go down to the garage to feed it. One day Fred Harrington got the bright idea of feeding the monkey ExLax. The results were that we didn't go to the garage much afterwards.

His future wife was North Creek's answer to Annie Oakley.
I always knew my wife Kathryn from town, because in North Creek you knew everyone else. That's just the way it was in a small town with party lines. Kathryn's parents owned the American Tavern in town and I would see her in school and when she was waiting tables at the hotel. Around 1940, I really began to see Kathryn and we became better acquainted. I knew she loved hunting and shooting, so naturally a safe way to ask her out was to ask her to go shooting. For our first date, we spent a romantic evening shooting rats at the town dump. That evening I took her dancing, which was more like a normal date. (They would share 55 years together before her passing in 1990.)

Thinking back, he admits "I can't say that I was a 'book worm' while attending high school. I played every sport available and when I wasn't playing a sport I was hunting, fishing, camping or skiing…. I sincerely feel that it was due to the values I learned as a boy that enabled me to enter the field of medicine where I got a chance to practice those values." Eventually he went to college at Holy Cross, and earned his M.D. degree in 1945 from Albany Medical College, joining the United States Air Force during the closing months of World War II. He finally completed a residency in the newly-created specialty of obstetrics and gynecology in 1951 (the year I was born).

By the time I arrived in Glens Falls to begin my medical career, Dr. Dan was already a legend in his field. Amazingly, he is one of thirty-three family members spanning four generations to become physicians, including two other Daniel O'Keeffes! He would deliver over ten thousand babies in his forty-year career. He would regale us at the physicians' lunch table in Glens Falls Hospital with his many anecdotes and stories about "the Crick". I learned about his family's migration from Québec in the mid nineteenth century, and about his Uncle Dan, once a pitcher for his Union College baseball team, who practiced his delivery growing up on a farm by throwing frozen cow dung at his sheep to get them moving! The only time I would avoid him was when I was in a hurry, because once I would begin to listen to him, his stories and bawdy jokes would make me forget I had work to do. One such story which he recounted in his book *You Really Made Housecalls?* went as follows:

One afternoon a very pleasant, elderly woman came to my office and as was my habit, I began asking her what I felt were relevant questions, writing her history down as I went. "So tell me," I began. "Do you and your husband still have intercourse?"
"Wait a minute," she responded. "I'll have to ask my husband." With that she popped her head out of the examining room door and called to him. He came down the hallway, a concern look on his face.
"Tom, do we still have intercourse?" She asked him.
Tom's response was, "I told you one hundred times. All we have is Blue Cross and Blue Shield."

During the many years that he ran his busy OB/GYN practice without any partners, he worked hours that now seem impossible to believe:

I would have to be in surgery and ready to operate or assist by 8 AM, whether I had been up all night delivering babies or not. Surgery went from 8:00 to noon or 1 PM. Then I would make my rounds of previous surgical patients and deal with any problems or concerns. I would be at the office from roughly 1:30 to 5:30 PM, occasionally being pulled out for a delivery. .. And later, of course, as more and more women join the work force, I had to accommodate their career schedules. So, on Mondays and Wednesdays I extended my office hours into the evening and saw patients from 7:00 PM to 10:00 PM and on Saturday mornings…. On the evenings I didn't have late office hours, I would make my rounds again at the hospital. Most nights, when I arrived home around 11:00 or so, I would be called out again for a delivery. In truth, I rarely slept through a whole night…. One night I was called out for the third time and being tired and in a hurry, I neglected to raise the garage door and I backed right through it… I can distinctly remember one night when I got to sleep through the entire night from the time my head hit the pillow. Of course it was toward the end of my career. I recall it so vividly because when I woke up the next morning and realized that I hadn't had my sleep disturbed and it was actually morning, I was shocked…. There were many times during my practice when, either prior to or after the delivery, I would be so exhausted I would just fall asleep on a stretcher tucked somewhere away from foot traffic, in some corner of the hospital.

As if his practice didn't keep him busy enough, in 1955 he also became involved in medical politics through the Medical Society of the State of New York. By 1965 he was the president of the Society, and he continued to serve on the board of trustees for many years.

Such a workload has killed many a physician prematurely, but Dr. O'-Keeffe is alive and well at the age of 88 as I write this. He credits his longevity to a gut-wrenching decision he made back in 1991- one that many members of our profession find difficult- he retired. At the age of seventy after a forty-year career, still healthy enough to start a new life for himself, he quit while he was ahead. Looking back, he puts it this way:

I was fortunate enough to practice medicine at a time when I was able to take care of the indigent for nothing, when there was no government interference, no threats of litigation hanging over my head, and when the patient didn't think they knew more than the doctor did…. I was able to take the original Hippocratic Oath at a time when it meant something, when it was the gold standard by which we govern every action involving patient care, at a time when a doctor/patient relationship did not begin with the words, "what insurance coverage do you have?" or "the doctor expects your co-pay to be paid in advance."

"Until I retired," he told me, "I didn't have time for anything else but medicine. When Jim, then Kate (his son and daughter) joined my practice in 1977 and 1983, I began thinking about life after medicine. My father lived to be ninety-two; his three brothers were 94, 99, and 104 when they died. I figured I still had time to pick up some new hobbies, but at first I didn't know what to do with myself. My friend Bob Landry was quite a golfer, so he took me out for a lesson. I quit after the fourth hole. As luck would have it, Roy Emerson, the famous Australian tennis player, had been making appearances annually in Glens Falls for several years for the Red Cross and Youth Center, which I was also involved with. We became friends, and so I took up tennis, and I liked it! I took some lessons, and started playing pretty well. Roy and some other former pros started the Legends of Tennis in Brownsville Texas, so people like me could play against Wimbledon champs like Rod Laver, John Newcombe and Ken Rosewall. Roy signed me up, and that was 20 years ago. I've played tennis with some of the best players that ever lived, and I'm still playing today.

Not only does he play tennis, he wins at tennis-a lot. He won the New York State championship in doubles with his partner Ed Gall in 2006, and the gold medal at the National Senior Olympics in 2007 in his age bracket. He plays all winter in Sarasota, five or six days a week. "I've had my share of health problems, needing a permanent pacemaker in 2003… I broke my left wrist once, so I played tennis with a cast on my arm! But the Lord has been very good to me for letting me keep healthy and I believe that staying active is the key…. It seems as if I have lived three lives; the country boy in North Creek, the OB/GYN doctor in Glens Falls, and now the old geezer still having fun and enjoying life at age 88!" He still talks with pride about how he went paragliding in the Swiss Alps when he was eighty. He is actually looking forward to turning ninety so that he can compete in the 90+ age bracket of the National US Tennis Association Championship tournament. In his third book, Dan offers other advice for those seeking the fountain of youth:

Those who know me well, know I appreciate a good joke and a healthy sense of humor. I think that's what keeps me young-both physically and at heart, and that is a treatment I am quick to prescribe to anyone.

Maybe that is why I have so much respect for Dan O'Keeffe. He was willing to retire from medicine while still healthy, active, and adventurous. Too many physicians let the practice of medicine consume them. Physicians in particular neglect themselves and feel adrift without purpose when it is time to move on. Dan is living proof that you can have a successful medical career and still enjoy a second life after retirement, even if you have to reinvent yourself in the process.

In some circles, patient's friends and colleagues refer to me informally as Dr. Dan. But when Dr. Dan O'Keeffe entered the Owens House gallery that 2004 evening in North Creek, there was no doubt who the real Dr. Dan was.

Long live the *real* Dr. Dan!

140

140

DR. HERBERT SAVEL MD – RURAL INTERNIST AND ARTIST

Elizabethtown, October 2009

Herbert Savel, a primary care physician practicing in the tiny Adirondack community of Elizabethtown New York, compares the creation of art to driving a car toward a cliff. "If you stop short you're very safe, but it's boring. You've got to drive as fast as you can and then hit the brake right at the edge of the abyss- then you've got it. There has to be a challenge."

How's this for a challenge: run a solo medical practice for almost forty years while creating the first rural Veteran's Administration clinic in the nation, learn a nearly-extinct art form- traditional German wood carving- at the age of fifty-eight and set out to carve over 2500 works of art in your spare time. Better yet, make each carving represent a scene from the Holocaust and decline to profit from it. For Doctor Savel, it is no longer a challenge. It is a mission he has every intention of completing.

Success seems to come naturally to Herb Savel. A native of New York City, he earned a medical degree from NYU in 1958, obtained a Pharmacology degree from Yale and began a promising career in oncology at Memorial Sloan-Kettering Institute. After a thirteen-year career that included publishing over twenty articles and establishing an impeccable reputation as a teacher, scientist and clinician at such renowned facilities as the Brookhaven Laboratory and the University of Vermont, he gave it all up for the life of a country doctor in the Adirondacks. "I had had enough of the academic life" he explains. In that world, patients were not thought of as people; they were considered hearts, breasts, livers or other diseased organs. Instead, he found his life's work in Elizabethtown, New York.

Herbert Savel MD in his workshop

As a solo practitioner, Doctor Savel has been on duty around the clock, almost every day and night since 1971. While raising two sons with his wife Isabel, he enjoyed reading and abstract oil painting in his limited spare time. It was during a home visit one fateful day in 1992 that his life took an unexpected turn. "I made a house call on an elderly German-born man named Karl Huttig, who had fled from his home in Bavaria and hiked across the Alps to safety in Austria in 1933. Although a Catholic, he had to leave Germany when the Nazis came to power because his parents had previously emigrated to the United States, and that fact alone was sufficient to brand their entire family as traitors to the regime. I was amazed by the many beautiful wooden carvings in his home, and asked about them. They were *his* carvings. He had learned the traditional Alpine wood carving method in Germany, graduating from the State Woodcarving School in Oberammergau in 1933. Karl learned after World War II that all of his carving school classmates had been killed in the carnage of war. After his health had improved, I felt comfortable in asking him to teach me how to carve. He agreed, and I took lessons from him for two nights a week for five years until his death in 1997. Now I would become one of the last practitioners of this old art form, and I soon learned what I had to do with it." A product of a Russian father and Polish mother, Savel had lost many family members in the Holocaust. "My First Cousin Lou Savel, who served in the American Army in World War II found only three surviving members of the family right after the war and paid the Soviet Government $10,000 for exit permits for each, so that they would be permitted to leave Russia and emigrate to Israel." For Herb, the Nazi atrocities during World War II

An early carving of an execution scene

caust, starting with images of Nazi firing squads, emaciated death camp survivors, Anne Frank's arrest, haunted graveyards, Jewish partisan fighters, and families being led to the gas chamber. Over time his style evolved from complex scenes containing simple characters to simple portraits carved in great detail. The work stirred a previously unexpressed passion in him. When he discovered a book by Serge Klarsfeld entitled *French Children of the Holocaust* featuring photographs of 2500 different children who had been sent to the death camp in Auschwitz, he realized he had found the perfect outlet for his personal and artistic needs. On April 1, 2002, he began carving the children.

Like Dr. Savel, I practice medicine in the Adirondacks while pursuing an art form that overlaps with my professional work. But Herbert Savel has taken the process to a whole new level. Perhaps that is why I had to meet him- to witness his work first-hand and find out what makes him tick.

He graciously agreed to allow me to view his carvings in his office as he explained why he does what he does. "I like practicing medicine. It's a lot of fun and I'm good at it. I look forward to carving while I am seeing patients, and I look forward to seeing patients while I am carving. I enjoy helping people, and sometimes they're live people, and sometimes they're dead children. By taking a two-dimensional black-and-white image and turning it into a three-dimensional carving, I'm helping to memorialize the memory of a child." We were interrupted by a message that one of his veterans was coughing up large amounts of blood. "Get him an ambulance", he said to Isabel, who is also his office manager. I asked him how he finds time for his carving. "I carve on the weekends from morning till night," he replied, "and I carve on work days from after supper until bedtime, usually 6:30 to 11 PM. My wife enjoys sewing, knitting and playing music. When someone asked her 'what's it like having a husband who carves all the time,' she answers 'at least I know where he is!'" Another interruption from Isabel: "Mrs. Smith is having chest pain. What do you want to do?" "Tell her I'll see her in the emergency room." I could see his day was going to be hectic. I knew the feeling, but he was unperturbed. I asked him how many children's portraits he had done. Without hesitation, he replied "nine hundred and eighty three. Since I complete approximately 150 carvings per year, I estimate that it will take me about ten more years to carve portraits of all of the children in Klarsfeld's book." "When was

remain very personal. "My Cousin Mark Fogelgarn who was born in Poland the same year that I was born in the USA, was rounded up from the Lodz Ghetto and murdered. His parents, who survived the War, settled in Montreal after many years of fruitless searching in Europe for Mark." Dr. Savel's inspiration was to turn his family's tragedy into art.

Using historical photographs, he began carving scenes from the Holo-

the last day that you *didn't* carve?" I asked. He looked at me almost bemused, answering "April 1, 2002!"

Although I had hoped to see his workshop/studio, it would have to wait until another day, as he excused himself and headed for the ER. Instead I took in the hundreds of carvings that covered almost every square foot of his walls, awestruck by their composition, execution and cumulative impact. Deceptively simple in their style, they were carved with extreme precision and painted meticulously. In one scene a wounded partisan fighter lays dying on a cobblestone street, and I noticed that every cobblestone was individually carved, including their beveled edges, then painted so as to depict mud-spattered granite. The children's eyes featured deep-set pupils that would follow me all around the room. He had truly brought them to life on his walls. I felt humbled, devastated, but somehow comforted as well. At least they existed, thanks to a man who truly cared about every one of them.

On a muggy June afternoon in 2009 I returned to visit his home and watch him continue carving what he calls "A *Kaddish* in Wood", referring to the Jewish prayer for the dead. His workshop was neat, organized and well-equipped. Watching him create *kaddish* number 999, I could see the hands of a healer at work. "There's a lot of fun in using your hands to create something. The magic is when I carve, I'm re-creating these people." As he talked, his hands caressed the wood, and as the bas-relief image emerged, he related to it as though it was indeed alive. He finishes each carving with halos around each person's head- except the Nazis- explaining "my ancestors followed the *Kabbalah*, and believed that every human being has within him a divine spark which comes from God, and these halos represent what we humans have in common with each other." Choosing images from the Klarsfeld book isn't easy for him. "Sometimes I can almost hear the children telling me 'It's my turn! Me, me; do *me* next!'"

Once he begins a piece, it takes him five to twelve hours to complete it. "When I stare at the same photograph for hours, I become very familiar with them. I get to know them." When he has successfully brought a rendition of eleven-year-old Marie Jelen to life, it causes an involuntarily emotional response in him. Looking at his work as though he was looking at his own living granddaughter, he declares "I love you Marie! She's beautiful- and they killed her! Wow. It's up to me to show the world what she

looked like…she was gorgeous! I don't think the Holocaust has to be ugly. Their deaths were ugly, but these children were beautiful! Hers was a life that was squashed; terminated…"

Like most truly gifted physician-artists, Savel's creativity is fueled by an invaluable degree of obsessive-compulsiveness which is focused, laser-like, on his very personal mission. Another physician-artist, the famous psy-

A kaddish in wood

143

chiatrist Carl Jung, once said "Art is a kind of innate drive that seizes a human being and makes him its instrument. The artist is not a person endowed with free will who seeks his own ends, but one who allows art to realize its purpose through him." Jung could easily have been talking about Dr. Herb Savel.

"People ask me how I can do this. I've *got* to do it, because nobody else has done it and nobody else is *going* to do it.....It's ironic that the last German woodcarver in the tradition of authentic German woodcarving is a Jewish woodcarver carving the Holocaust. It makes me very happy- I have the feeling I'm doing something real. I love taking care of patients, I really do. But the carving is something that needs to be done." Already his works can be found in galleries and Holocaust museums, but they are not for

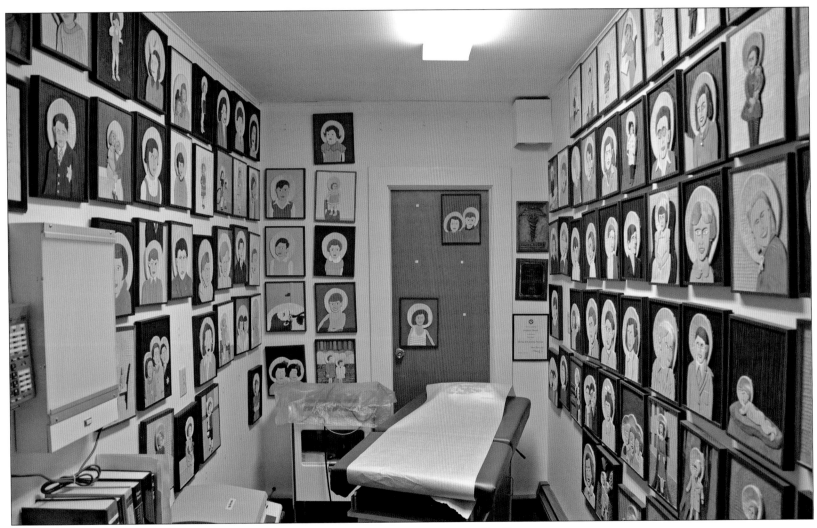

An examination room in Savel's office

144

sale "because they're too personal. I like to put them where people can see them and understand the Holocaust because... time has gone by. The generation that remembers it is pretty much gone, and when people say to me 'did they really kill young women and children and babies', I have to say yes, and this is a testimony."

Savel appears to be in good health, and as long as he draws breath, he will continue his *kaddish* until it is completed. Ultimately, what makes Herbert Savel tick is what makes every great artist tick. His passion for his art is what gives him the superhuman stamina to continue what he is doing. William Lester Stevens, an early twentieth century artist put it simply: "Don't paint to sell- *paint because you can't help it.*" Herb Savel carves because he can't help it. And the world is a little better for it.

Doctor Savel with one of his favorite carvings

JOHN RUGGE – CEO, HUDSON HEADWATERS HEALTH NETWORK

Warrensburg, August 2013

When I was an impressionable young fellow in the 1960's searching for a career path that would lead to a fulfilling life, I found myself reading the historical fiction of Dr. Frank G. Slaughter. Dr. Slaughter, who was both a physician and a very successful author (his 52 books sold over 60 million copies from the 1940's to the 1980's with such titles as *Buccaneer Doctor*, and *The Road to Bythinia; A Novel of Luke, the Beloved Physician*) was an inspiration. His books made physicians, especially those who toiled in rustic obscurity, seem like the most altruistic and noble of professionals. That role model, though fictional, was never completely extinguished by the grind of my seven years of graduate training. My ultimate goal during medical school in Hershey, Pennsylvania and residency in Bay Shore, Long Island was to return to my hometown of Glens Falls. Although Harriet and I hoped to one day set up a Family Medicine practice in the Adirondacks, we had no clear plan on how to make it happen. It was on a summer's day in 1980 while working at the Glens Falls Hospital emergency room that I first met Dr. John Rugge. That meeting changed my life.

I had taken the ER job as a way of returning to Glens Falls and providing my family with a steady income. This was important since my wife, although a physician, was unemployed and very pregnant with our first child. The job turned out to be a perfect way to meet and become part of the medical community. I soon began hearing about this near-mythical rural doctor who had been trained as an ordained minister at Harvard before going on to medical school, a man who had written a book about camping and paddling canoes in the Labrador wilderness, and who had accidentally created a small network of rural health centers in the Adirondacks. My boss, Dr. Fritz Hauser, who knew of my Adirondack roots and

Family Medicine training, kept telling me "You really should meet Dr. Rugge- he is a remarkable man, and he could probably use you."

That fateful meeting occurred when an ambulance emblazoned with "WARRENSBURG EMERGENCY" on the back doors pulled up the ER ramp, which burst open to reveal a tall, red-headed figure assisting the squad members with a critically ill patient. Although he seemed calm and unassuming in appearance, his dramatic entry cast him in a somewhat swashbuckling light. I followed him and the patient into an empty room where, as we waited for the patient to be transferred from the ambulance stretcher to our Gurney table, I turned to him and said "Doctor Rugge, I presume?" Turning toward me and noticing the name tag on my white coat, he replied, "Aah, you're Doctor Way. Fritz has told me about you." I suddenly knew what it must have been like when Henry Stanley met Dr. Livingstone, (although we were not in darkest Africa and neither of us was suffering from malaria).

The word 'swashbuckling' is rarely used these days to describe John Rugge, but his visionary boldness and daring accomplishments over the course of his life and medical career could make the word fit quite accurately. The fact that many of these achievements seemed to have happened either by accident or without a premeditated plan makes them all the more impressive.

"My grandfather was Harry Vickers," John told me, "the first person in my mother's family to have left the farm and gone to college—that being Albany Medical College from which he graduated in 1907. He died before I was born but remains a family legend. He treated minor and serious illness, pulled teeth, did surgery, (removing tonsils on the kitchen table, removing his younger son's appendix), and made house calls by horse and sleigh. When he died, the entire Little Falls hospital staff marched in his funeral procession, and every flag in the city was lowered to half-mast."

Although his grandfather was a revered small-town physician, John was not inclined to follow that path. In fact, after receiving a degree in philosophy from Williams College, John attended Harvard Divinity School despite having no desire to become a man of the cloth. "It was a question of modes of describing human behavior", he told Bernard Carman in *Adirondack Life* in 1981. "Somehow at Williams the freshest and most stimulating seemed to be not in philosophy, but in religion." While at Harvard, he spent time studying human behavior in a psychiatric hospital. "While at Mass Mental Health Hospital, six of us divinity students were assigned to the psychiatrist-in-chief with three of us eventually switching to medical school. Dr. Terry Maltzberger was quite the influence, but I think of my

decision to go to medical school as more like a 'conversion experience.' One evening in a cubicle at the university library it occurred to me: I should be a doctor. Chalk it up to Harry Vickers and Terry Maltzberger in equal measure."

John's experiences as a Boy Scout kindled a love for the outdoors, and a Scout canoeing trip from Raquette to Tupper Lakes when he was eleven gave him his first taste of paddling a canoe in Adirondack waters. In 1959, John and his father went down the Hudson River Gorge for the first time, kindling a lifelong interest in white-water paddling. While in medical school at Yale, he met James West Davidson, a PhD candidate, and discovered that they were both independently researching a possible canoe trip to Canada's Labrador wilderness. They joined forces and not only went on an expedition that covered over two hundred miles of remote rivers and rapids far from civilization, but also decided to write a book about it entitled *The Complete Wilderness Paddler* that is still noted as one of the best paddling guides in print. Comparing their adventure to that of Huckleberry Finn, as they explained in their introduction, "Huck was a fellow who felt 'sivilization' closing in too tight around him, so tight that he had to leave for awhile. To get away he chose a river, and after his trip was over he wrote a passably good book about his adventures." So did John. Over the last forty years, John's name has been almost as synonymous with paddling as with rural health care, and he uses canoeing as an analogy for his day job. "Some routes through white water are better than others," he says; "some strokes are more appropriate at a given instant."

In 1974, after graduation from Yale and completing a one-year internship at Albany Medical Center, John was looking for temporary employment near the white waters of the upper Hudson River before beginning a three-year residency in Family Medicine at Albany Medical Center. He wanted to spend a few months working on his

John Rugge relaxing on a cannon in Saint Maarten- March 8, 2008

book manuscript while paddling and practicing a little medicine. As it happened, the Glens Falls Hospital was looking for a physician to supervise a group of Physician Assistants hired by the hospital to provide health care to the people of Chestertown. That Adirondack community had just lost all three of its general practitioners to retirement and relocation. Chestertown happened to be situated between the Schroon and Hudson Rivers, John explained. "It was a chance to practice rural medicine in a somewhat novel way, and that proved exciting enough that I deferred for one more year going back to Albany." As it turned out, John never went back to Albany (until much later to confer with the governor and legislators as the CEO of Hudson Headwaters). Although he planned to move on after six months, he found he could not. Instead he was made to feel at home by the town's grateful population of Adirondackers. Perhaps his background in theology, history and philosophy played a role: "How do you leave a little town that has no doctors?" he explains. When Warrensburg's last physician retired in 1976 after no longer being able to endure a work day that regularly ended at one o'clock in the morning, it was déjà vu, and he now presided over a 'network' of two health centers. He soon learned, however, that there was more to his job than just practicing medicine; he had administrative duties as well. When he received a letter from the state health department threatening to close down the Chester

John in an early White Water Derby

Health Center due to its dilapidated appearance, he helped a dozen local volunteers paint the building in one weekend. To keep the gossamer-thin money stream going, he learned the art of securing state and federal grants, which involved becoming an articulate, passionate, and sincere spokesman for the practice or rural primary care. He discovered he was good at it, and over the years he has found enough physicians, PAs, nurses, and administrators to staff the expanding number of health centers that included the addition of Indian Lake and North Creek in 1981, Bolton Landing in 1985, and many more since then. But in January of

2013, when he was asked by Gordon Woodworth of the Glens Falls' *The Chronicle* whether he had a vision back in the early days of where he would be today, he replied honestly, "not even a glimmer." And as if his core duties as family doctor, administrator, CEO, and advocate for primary care weren't enough to keep him busy, he also served as the Warren County coroner for over seventeen years.

As John took me on a recruiting tour to his four health centers in Warren and Hamilton County in the summer of 1981, he spoke about the challenges of creating and sustaining small medical offices in such hamlets as North Creek, Chestertown, Indian Lake and Warrensburg. I was immediately impressed by his intuitive grasp of what needed to be done to create and expand a network of rural health centers, and how to go about doing it. I recall commenting to him, "It sounds like we are either going to have to get larger or smaller to survive." Little did I know how far ahead of me he was on the matter. John had already recruited Harriet in November 1980 to work two or three half-days a week at the Chester Health Center, and I appreciated his willingness to accommodate her needs as both mother and physician- it made good business sense. When John hired me eight months later, Harriet and I represented half of the total number of physicians in the network, in addition to the five midlevel providers already employed. Over time, his altruism, honesty, and eerily prescient business sense has been embraced by local leaders in other communities, including Schroon Lake, Ticonderoga, and, later, Glens Falls, Moreau, Queensbury, Moriah, and Fort Edward. As I write this, there are more than 600 network employees in the Hudson Headwaters Health Network, including approximately 50 physicians, three dentists, 80 mid-levels and two podiatrists, generating 285,000 visits by over 70,000 patients at fifteen facilities in six counties in and around the Adirondacks, with an annual budget of $62 million. Not a bad record for a divinity and medical school graduate with only one year of internship under his belt. If that's not swashbuckling, then I don't know what is!

Neither I nor any of my fellow HHHN employees can imagine how anyone but John could have built a successful rural health care network. He may not have known exactly what he was doing along the way, but to the casual (and even the not-so-casual) observer, it seemed like he had planned the whole thing from the beginning. Glenn Fish, a former chairman of the HHHN board of directors, once said of him, "The canoeist must be able to move faster than the current, and John Rugge has been in the forefront of the health care current in establishing team health care." Well put. We have all wondered about John's plans for retirement. When Gordon Woodworth asked him what would be his legacy, he replied "I've been trying to tell everybody (that) in my mid-career position, it's hard for me to imagine a legacy. Retirement? What's that?... I'm just beginning to learn the ropes!"

October 8, 2008

Having lived and worked in and around of the Adirondack Park for so many years, I try not to take my world for granted. With my hectic day job, it is hard to spend the time I would like exploring the park's myriad lakes, ponds, rivers, and mountains. I have climbed less than a half-dozen of the forty-six High Peaks, and don't expect to ever climb them all. So, when my schedule does not permit a climb or a paddle, I will read books like Paul Jamieson's *The Adirondack Reader*. This remarkable book contains excerpts from the earliest and most historic writings of the legendary explorers who were the first to witness the raw beauty of the Adirondacks. The book also includes an account of the first known climb up Mount Marcy, the highest of all the High Peaks. It mentions the man most often associated with Marcy, the peculiarly articulate nineteenth century guide Orson "Old Mountain" Phelps, who climbed the mountain over one hundred times and described the rapture of standing on its summit as "a feeling of heaven uph'istedness." My favorite author is Phelps' contemporary Seneca Ray Stoddard, whose extraordinary photographs of the Adirondack wilderness were matched by his colorful prose. It was Stoddard's words more than any one else, written in his first guidebook *The Adirondacks* in 1875 that made me realize

Dennis Phillips and I feeling "heaven uph'isted"

that, at least once in my life, I had to climb Mount Marcy:

Come with me up into a high mountain! …Over a rippling ocean of forests first, their long swelling waves, now rising, now sinking down into deep hollows, here in grand mountains, crested as with caps of foam, there tormented by counter currents into wildly dashing shapes, like ocean billows, frozen by Divine command, their summit-glittering granite, their deep green troughs, gleaming with threads of silver and bits of fallen sky.

In the summer of 2008 I had a conversation with my friend Dennis Phillips, an attorney who specializes in land ownership disputes within the Adirondack Park. He had studied the Finch, Pruyn Company's stewardship of 161,000 acres of land in and around the High Peaks prior to its sale to the Nature Conservancy in 2007, and he was discussing how much he treasured the Adirondacks when we both realized that neither of us had ever climbed Marcy. We decided that it was too important a goal to keep putting off until our knees and backs had put it beyond our reach forever, and so we agreed to cross it off our 'bucket list' on Wednesday October 8, 2008.

Fortunately, four days after a snowfall in the High Peaks, October 8th was a sunny and seasonably warm day, with a light breeze from the southwest. I thought it an important statement that we had both taken the day off from our professions to experience this adventure, as a way of rekindling our work-weary spirits.

Heading north in the dark from Glens Falls, Dennis and I shared many stories that revealed how much we both had grown to love these mountains and their people. He had studied lands owned by The Ausable Club, the Brandreth family and others, while I had driven many of the back roads in Warren, Essex and Hamilton counties to visit patients and photograph the landscapes. He had encountered the landowners, businesspeople, environmentalists, bush pilots and local politicians, while I had come to know the hermits, trappers, guides, woodsmen and regular Adirondack folks whose family ties to the land went back over two centuries.

As we arrived in the Keene Valley, the first light of dawn was reflecting off some high cirrus clouds to the northeast. Our excitement grew as we parked in the nearly-deserted parking lot at Adirondak Loj and pulled on our packs. I made sure my Nikon D-80 had 4 GB of memory and two fully-charged batteries while Dennis signed us in at the trailhead. Soon we were on our way. He laughed at some of the colloquialisms I had learned from my patients, such

Looking toward the MacIntyre range

On the trail

as Howard Meade's announcement "I'm as happy as a toad in a thunderstorm!" and Bonnie Cleveland telling me I had given her a medicine "that would grow hair on a crowbar!" He regaled me with his account of flying over the rolling western Adirondacks in his many autumn trips to his hunting camp on Bear Pond.

My Nikon got as much of a workout as our legs while we made our way up the mountain, with many of my images featuring Dennis' unsuspecting backside for perspective. Soon we stopped at Mary Dam to watch the sun climb over the trees and cast its golden glow off the MacIntyre Range. Continuing along Phelps Brook, named for the old guide, the crisp mountain air carried the familiar tartness of decaying leaves as our boots rustled through them. We encountered few other hikers on this mid-week day, and our thoughts wandered to pleasant places. I told Dennis of a recent meeting I had with Clarence Petty, the 103-year-old guide, forest ranger, conservationist and surveyor who had been at the forefront of protecting the Adirondack wilderness.

   Up and up we went, until we encountered an Austrian gentleman in his seventies at Indian Falls who was hiking and camping alone. Although he had explored the length and breadth of the Alps, he was nonetheless impressed with our Adirondacks. "Not as high, but just as beautiful!" he exclaimed.

Continuing our climb, I thought of Stoddard's description of his Marcy ascent over 130 years earlier:

Now the trees of the valley glide away behind us; the dark spruce and pine; and the sturdy balsam climbing the mountainside- tall and graceful at first, but growing smaller as they rise; now gnarled and twisted and scarce above the surface, sending their branches out

Marcy Dam Pond

close along the ground, their white tops bleached and ghastly, like dead roots of upturned trees, the hardy lichens still higher, then comes naked rock, and we stand on the wind-swept summit of the Adirondacks, "Tahawus," the cloud-splitter of the Indian.

Approaching a fork in the trail that would take us to either John's Brook Lodge or to our mountaintop destination, we came to a clearing where we could see the summit for the first time, with a remnant of the recent snowfall still draped across its shoulders. After hiking for three hours it seemed awfully far away, but we slogged on through the swampy area between Marcy and Little Marcy summits and soon began carefully scrambling up the ice-covered granite above the tree line. With Haystack Mountain and Panther Gorge looming ahead on our left, the view I saw

Denis with an Austrian hiker

souls, never to be forgotten. Apparently, the experience affected Stoddard in much the same way as he stood atop Tahawus, the Cloud Splitter:

Around their chief cluster the other great peaks- East, West, North, South; limitless, numberless, a confused mass of peaks and ridges, gathering, crowding close up to the base of the one on which we stand, and receding in waves of deep, then tender green, all down through the scale of color to its blue and purple edge; pen cannot convey an idea of its sublimity, the pencil fails to even suggest the blended strength and delicacy of the scene. The rude laugh is hushed, the boisterous shout dies out on reverential lips, the body shrinks down, feeling its own littleness, the soul expands, and rising above the earth, claims kinship with its Creator, questioning not his existence.

We stayed on the summit as long as we could, eating our lunch, taking with my own eyes was far more beautiful than any mere photograph. Panther Gorge was so deep that I couldn't even see the bottom, while Haystack looked so close that it seemed I could reach it with a nine-iron shot, though it was a mile away. Following the designated path to avoid damaging the fragile arctic tundra foliage, we were forced to struggle through wet snow and ice in the shaded areas until finally, after four and a half hours, we made it to the top. We were not disappointed.

We found ourselves atop the highest point in the Adirondacks, and the world was literally at our feet. The view in every direction was spectacular, and it made us feel small and insignificant. We read the plaque placed on Marcy's summit in 1937 that commemorated the anniversary of its first ascent a century before. The plaque, as old as it was, looked brand-new compared to the mottled, lichen-encrusted, billion-year-old granite in which it was embedded. Completely surrounded by wilderness in all directions, we were mesmerized. Dennis' cell phone was buzzing away with incessant emails, but he didn't answer them. The work that awaited me at the Indian Lake Health Center seemed a million miles away. We soaked in the view, absorbing it into our

Denis approaching the summit

155

pictures of each other, calling our spouses to let them know that we had actually made it to the top, watching the sun move across the sky, until at last we had to head back to civilization. After returning to the car at dusk, we enjoyed a nice meal in Lake Placid, where I ordered the appropriately-named Mount Marcy Platter while savoring Long Trail draft beer. Heading home, our spirits felt cleansed and renewed. The day reminded us that living and working in the Adirondacks is truly a privilege. We stood where Stoddard and Phelps had stood, and we were "heaven up-h'ised."

Haystack Mountain across Panther Gorge

156

Boreas Pond from Mount Marcy

157

ACKNOWLEDGEMENTS

It took eight years and a lot of work to create this book. Although the stories and color photographs are almost all my own, the efforts of many other people were necessary for you to be reading this now.

Most importantly, the people whose stories you have just read were kind and generous enough to share their personal lives with me. They trusted me to tell their stories accurately and with all the respect and affection I feel for them. They even signed HIPAA consent forms to make it legal for me to write about their medical problems. The war veterans and their families were particularly generous in sharing their experiences with me and allowing me to scan their diaries, photo albums, and other personal memorabilia. This book is about them, and for them. I have kept my promise to make them all immortal- if only in literature.

This book would not have been nearly as readable without the endless patience and timeless support of my wife Harriet, whose editing skills greatly enhanced the manuscript, making it flow better and correcting my tendency to write long, wordy run-on sentences. (Oops – there's another one.) I owe her big time… and I'm sure I will pay – somehow!

When Larry Bauer, CEO of the Family Medicine Education Consortium contacted me in 2010 with an offer to bring the illustrated stories of my medical career to a broader audience, I wasn't sure I was up to the task. He convinced me I was, and his support has helped me appreciate the universal relevance of my work. Although I live in and write about the people of the Adirondacks, their stories teach lessons that apply to all humanity. It is a great honor to have the FMEC's support when I needed it most.

Howard Nelson, the Director of the Hudson Headwaters Health Network Foundation, also encouraged me along the way. With his help we can use this book to raise awareness of the vital role that HHHN plays in maintaining the health of the people of northeastern New York State while serving as a model for primary care across the United States.

Elizabeth Folwell and the editors of Adirondack Life magazine have supported and encouraged me to write these stories over the years. The faces and stories of Dr. Herbert Savel, Greg George, Frank Lillibridge, Dan Moore and Ed Bennett first appeared in Adirondack Life, and are included in this book in modified form with the magazine's consent. I also used the magazine as a reference for my stories about Dr. John Rugge and Nathan Farb.

Other sources of information and photographs include the Trudeau Institute's image of Dr. Edward Livingston Trudeau and Larry Wilke's picture of a young John Rugge going down the Hudson- sideways!

Finally, I would like to thank Nancy Best and all the staff of Nancy Did It Publishing of Blossvale, New York for their efficient and professional work. Improving the cover and doing all the layouts over several months, they turned a manuscript with over 100 illustrations into the final product you now hold in your hands. Nancy made my eight-year-long dream come true.

BIBLIOGRAPHY

FOREWORD

The Intellectual Basis of Family Medicine G. Gayle Stephens, MD
Society of Family Teachers 1982

Thomas L. Leaman, MD
Founding Chair - Department of Family and Community Medicine, Pennsylvania State University School of Medicine

ADIRONDACKS

The High Peaks of Essex: The Adirondack Mountains of Orson Schofield Phelps Bill Healy, Purple Mountain Press, Fleishmanns, NY 1992

The Adirondacks Illustrated Seneca Ray Stoddard, Weed, Parsons & Co. Albany, NY 1874

The Adirondack Reader Paul Jamieson, MacMillan Books, New York NY, 1964

BARBARA ROSS

An Adirondack Archive: The Trail to Windover Elizabeth Hudnut Clarkson, North Country Books, Utica, NY 1993

RICHARD GARRETT

Adirondack Life magazine "The Adirondack Regiment" Daniel Way, March-April 2011

FRANK LILLIBRIDGE

Adirondack Life magazine "One Simple Life" January-February 1997

THE SMITH FAMILY

Ancient Futures: Lessons from Ladakh for a Globalizing World Helena Norberg-Hodge, Sierra Club Books, San Francisco, CA 1991

CLARENCE PETTY

Adirondack Explorer magazine, www.adirondackexplorer.org, Saranac Lake, NY, May/June 2006 issue, March/April 2007

The Extraordinary Life of Clarence Petty Christopher Angus, Syracuse University Press, Syracuse New York 2003

NATHAN FARB

"Nathan Farb: Behind the Scenes" Alex Shoumatoff, *Adirondack Life*, Volume XXVII September/October 1996

COUNTRY DOCTORS

Country Doctor; His Endless Work Has its Own Rewards E Eugene Smith Life Magazine September 20, 1948

Country Doctor; Practicing Medicine the Old-Fashioned Way Glen Dowling and Lynn Johnson; Life Magazine June 1998

Confessions of a Sin Eater; A Doctor's Reflections Therese Zink 2012

Down From Troy Richard Seltzer; William Morrow and Co., Inc. New York 1992

Pulse – Voices From the Heart of Medicine Paul Gross MD and Diane Guernsey, Change in health care Publishing, New Rochelle, NY 2010

The Country Doctor Revisited: A Twenty-First Century Reader Therese Zink, editor, Kent State University Press, Kent, Ohio 2010

The Likes of Us Stu Cohen, David Godine Publishing, Jaffrey, NH 2009

The Recollections of a Country Doctor James A. Holley MD Meador Publishing Co. Boston 1939

What Matters in Medicine; Lessons From a Life in Primary Care David Loxtercamp MD, University of Michigan Press, Ann Arbor MI, 2013

DANIEL O'KEEFFE MD
Halfway to Heaven – Livin' in the "Crick" Dr. Dan O'Keeffe II Sunset Enterprises Queensbury NY, 2001

One Heartbeat from Heaven – The Story of the O'Keeffe Hunting Camp 1915-1965 Dr. Dan O'Keeffe II, Sunset Enterprises Queensbury NY, 2007

"You Really Made Housecalls?" The Practice and Politics of Medicine Dr. Dan O'Keeffe 2009

HERBERT SAVEL MD
Kaddish in Wood: Memorial Woodcarvings – The Children Dr. Herbert Savel, The Florida Holocaust Museum, St. Peters Florida 2009

Kaddish in Wood: Memorial Woodcarvings – Ghettos, Camps and Partisans Dr. Herbert Savel, The Florida Holocaust Museum, St. Peters Florida 2010

http://web.mac.com/hsavel/Kaddish_in_Wood/Home.html
http://alumni.med.nyu.edu/node/517
http://www.youtube.com/watch?v=bBEWaC9yvW4
http://www.youtube.com/watch?v=9oYRgDVxc9g
http://www.youtube.com/watch?v=bYF-SmFXyZc

JOHN RUGGE
"John Rugge and Dirty Rug" Bernard Carman, *Adirondack Life*, Volume XII July/August 1981

The Complete Wilderness Paddler James West Davidson and John Rugge, Alfred A Knopf, New York 1981

The Road to Bithynia – A Novel of Luke, the Beloved Physician Frank G. Slaughter, Doubleday & Co. New York NY 1951

ONE LAST LOOK
The Adirondacks; Illustrated Seneca Ray Stoddard, Van Benthuysen & Sons, Albany, NY 1875